Collins

2022 GUIDE
to the
NIGHT SKY

SOUTHERN HEMISPHERE

Storm Dunlop and Wil Tirion

Published by Collins
An imprint of HarperCollins*Publishers*
Westerhill Road, Bishopbriggs, Glasgow G64 2QT
www.harpercollins.co.uk

HarperCollins*Publishers*
1st Floor, Watermarque Building, Ringsend Road, Dublin 4, Ireland

© HarperCollins Publishers 2021
Text and illustrations © Storm Dunlop and Wil Tirion
Photographs © see acknowledgements page 110.

The contents of this publication are believed correct at the time of printing.
Nevertheless the publisher can accept no responsibility for errors or omissions,
changes in the detail given or for any expense or loss thereby caused.

HarperCollins does not warrant that any website mentioned in this title will be provided uninterrupted,
that any website will be error free, that defects will be corrected, or that the website or the server that
makes it available are free of viruses or bugs. For full terms and conditions please refer to the site
terms provided on the website.

A catalogue record for this book is available from the British Library

ISBN 978-0-00-846980-1

10 9 8 7 6 5 4 3 2 1

Printed in China by RR Donnelley APS

If you would like to comment on any aspect of this book, please contact us at the above address or online.
e-mail: collinsmaps@harpercollins.co.uk

 facebook.com/CollinsAstronomy

 @CollinsAstro

MIX
Paper from
responsible sources
FSC
www.fsc.org **FSC™ C007454**

This book is produced from independently certified
FSC™ paper to ensure responsible forest management.

For more information visit: www.harpercollins.co.uk/green

Contents

Introduction

The aim of this Guide is to help people find their way around the night sky, by showing how the stars that are visible change from month to month and by including details of various events that occur throughout the year. The objects and events described may be observed with the naked eye, or nothing more complicated than a pair of binoculars.

The conditions for observing naturally vary over the course of the year. During the summer, twilight may persist throughout the night and make it difficult to see the faintest stars. There are three recognized stages of twilight: civil twilight, when the Sun is less than 6° below the horizon; nautical twilight, when the Sun is between 6° and 12° below the horizon; and astronomical twilight, when the Sun is between 12° and 18° below the horizon. Full darkness occurs only when the Sun is more than 18° below the horizon. During nautical twilight, only the very brightest (navigation) stars are visible. During astronomical twilight, the faintest stars visible to the naked eye may be seen directly overhead, but are lost at lower altitudes. At Sydney, full darkness persists for about six hours at mid-summer. Even at Christchurch, NZ (not shown), full darkness lasts about four hours. By contrast, as far south as Cape Horn, at mid-summer nautical twilight persists, so only the very brightest stars are visible.

Another factor that affects the visibility of objects is the amount of moonlight in the sky. At Full Moon, it may be very difficult to see some of the fainter stars and objects, and even when the Moon is at a smaller phase it may seriously interfere with visibility if it is near the stars or planets in which you are interested. A full lunar calendar is given for each month and may be used to see when nights are likely to be darkest and best for observation.

The celestial sphere

All the objects in the sky (including the Sun, Moon and stars) appear to lie at some indeterminate distance on a large sphere, centred on the Earth. This *celestial sphere* has various reference points and features that are related to those of the Earth. If the Earth's rotational axis is extended, for example, it points to the North and South Celestial Poles, which are thus in line with the North and South Poles on Earth. Similarly, the *celestial equator* lies in the same plane as the Earth's equator,

The duration of twilight throughout the year at Sydney and Cape Horn.

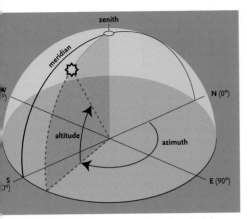

Measuring altitude and azimuth on the celestial sphere.

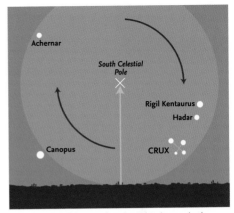

The altitude of the South Celestial Pole equals the observer's latitude.

and divides the sky into northern and southern hemispheres. Because this Guide is written for use in the southern hemisphere, the area of the sky that it describes includes the whole of the southern celestial hemisphere and those portions of the northern that become visible at different times of the year. Stars in the far north, however, remain invisible throughout the year, and are not included.

It is useful to know some of the special terms for various parts of the sky. As seen by an observer, half of the celestial sphere is invisible, below the horizon. The point directly overhead is known as the **zenith**, and the (invisible) one below one's feet as the **nadir**. The line running from the north point on the horizon, up through the zenith and then down to the south point is the **meridian**. This is an important invisible line in the sky, because objects are highest in the sky, and thus easiest to see, when they cross the meridian. Objects are said to **transit**, when they cross this line in the sky.

In this book, reference is frequently made in the text and in the diagrams to the standard compass points around the horizon. The position of any object in the sky may be described by its **altitude** (measured in degrees above the horizon), and its **azimuth** (measured in degrees from north 0°, through east 90°,

south 180° and west 270°). Experienced amateurs and professional astronomers also use another system of specifying locations on the celestial sphere, but that need not concern us here, where the simpler method will suffice.

The celestial sphere appears to rotate about an invisible axis, running between the North and South Celestial Poles. The location (i.e., the altitude) of the Celestial Poles depends entirely on the observer's position on Earth or, more specifically, their latitude. The charts in this book are produced for the latitude of 35°S, so the South Celestial Pole (SCP) is 35° above the southern horizon. The fact that the SCP is fixed relative to the horizon means that all the stars within 35° of the pole are always above the horizon and may, therefore, always be seen at night, regardless of the time of year. The southern circumpolar region is an ideal place to begin learning the sky, and ways to identify the circumpolar stars and constellations will be described shortly.

The ecliptic and the zodiac

Another important line on the celestial sphere is the Sun's apparent path against the background stars – in reality the result of the Earth's orbit around the Sun. This is known as the **ecliptic**. The point where the Sun, apparently moving along the ecliptic,

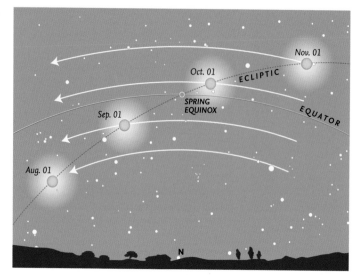

The Sun crossing the celestial equator at the September equinox (spring equinox in the southern hemisphere).

crosses the celestial equator from south to north is known as the (southern) autumn equinox, which occurs on March 20 or 21. At this time and at the (southern) spring equinox, on September 22 or 23, when the Sun crosses the celestial equator from north to south, day and night are almost exactly equal in length. (There is a slight difference, but that need not concern us here.) The March equinox is currently located in the constellation of Pisces, and is important in astronomy because it defines the zero point for a system of celestial coordinates, which is, however, not used in this Guide.

The Moon and planets are to be found in a band of sky that extends 8° on either side of the ecliptic. This is because the orbits of the Moon and planets are inclined at various angles to the ecliptic (i.e., to the plane of the Earth's orbit). This band of sky is known as the zodiac and, when originally devised, consisted of twelve **constellations**, all of which were considered to be exactly 30° wide. When the constellation boundaries were formally established by the International Astronomical Union in 1930, the exact extent of most constellations was altered and, nowadays, the ecliptic passes through thirteen constellations.

Because of the boundary changes, the Moon and planets may actually pass through several other constellations that are adjacent to the original twelve.

The constellations

Since ancient times, the celestial sphere has been divided into various constellations, most dating back to antiquity and usually associated with certain myths or legendary people and animals. Nowadays, the boundaries of the constellations have been fixed by international agreement and their names (in Latin) are largely derived from Greek or Roman originals. Some of the names of the most prominent stars are of Greek or Roman origin, but many are derived from Arabic names. Many bright stars have no individual names and, for many years, stars were identified by terms such as 'the star in Hercules' right foot'. A more sensible scheme was introduced by the German astronomer Johannes Bayer in the early seventeenth century. Following his scheme – which is still used today – most of the brightest stars are identified by a Greek letter followed by the genitive form of the constellation's Latin name. An example is the Pole Star, also known as Polaris and α

Ursae Minoris (abbreviated α UMi). The Greek alphabet is shown on page 110 and a list of all the constellations that may be seen from latitude 35°S, together with abbreviations, their genitive forms and English names is on page 109. Other naming schemes exist for fainter stars, but are not used in this book.

Asterisms

Apart from the constellations (88 of which cover the whole sky), certain groups of stars, which may form a part of a larger constellation or cross several constellations, are readily recognizable and have been given individual names. These groups are known as *asterisms*, and the most famous (and well-known to northern observers) is the 'Plough', the common name for the seven brightest stars in the constellation of Ursa Major, the Great Bear. The names and details of some asterisms mentioned in this book are given in the list on page 110.

Magnitudes

The brightness of a star, planet or other body is frequently given in magnitudes (mag.). This is a mathematically defined scale where larger numbers indicate a fainter object. The scale extends beyond the zero point to negative numbers for very bright objects. (Sirius, the brightest star in the sky is mag. -1.4.) Most observers are able to see stars to about mag. 6, under very clear skies.

The Moon

Although the daily rotation of the Earth carries the sky from east to west, the Moon gradually moves eastwards by approximately its diameter (about half a degree) in an hour. Normally, in its orbit around the Earth, the Moon passes above or below the direct line between Earth and Sun (at New Moon) or outside the area obscured by the Earth's shadow (at Full Moon). Occasionally, however, the three bodies are more-or-less perfectly aligned to give an *eclipse*: a solar eclipse at New Moon or a lunar eclipse at Full Moon. Depending on the exact circumstances, a solar eclipse may be merely partial (when the Moon does not cover the whole of the Sun's disk); annular (when the Moon is too far from Earth in its orbit to appear large enough to hide the whole of the Sun); or total. Total and annular eclipses are visible from very restricted areas of the Earth, but partial eclipses are normally visible over a wider area.

Somewhat similarly, at a lunar eclipse, the Moon may pass through the outer zone of the Earth's shadow, the *penumbra* (in a penumbral eclipse, which is not generally perceptible to the naked eye), so that just part of the Moon is within the darkest part of the Earth's shadow, the *umbra* (in a partial eclipse); or completely within the umbra (in a total eclipse). Unlike solar eclipses, lunar eclipses are visible from large areas of the Earth.

Occasionally, as it moves across the sky, the Moon passes between the Earth and individual planets or distant stars, giving rise to an *occultation*. As with solar eclipses, such occultations are visible from restricted areas of the world.

The planets

Because the planets are always moving against the background stars, they are treated in some detail in the monthly pages and information is given when they are close to other planets, the Moon or any of five bright stars that lie near the ecliptic. Such events are known as *appulses* or, more frequently, as *conjunctions*. (There are technical differences in the way these terms are defined – and should be used – in astronomy, but these need not concern us here.) The positions of the planets are shown for every month on a special chart of the ecliptic.

The term conjunction is also used when a planet is either directly behind or in front of the Sun, as seen from Earth. (Under normal circumstances it will then be invisible.) The conditions of most favourable visibility depend on whether the planet is one of the two known as *inferior planets* (Mercury and Venus) or one of the three *superior planets* (Mars, Jupiter and Saturn) that are covered in detail. (Some details of the fainter superior planets, Uranus and

Inferior planet.

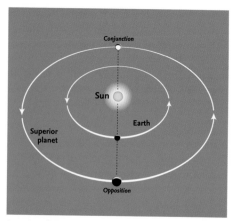

Superior planet.

Neptune, are included in this Guide, and special charts for both are given on page 25.)

The inferior planets are most readily seen at eastern or western **elongation**, when their angular distance from the Sun is greatest. For superior planets, they are best seen at **opposition**, when they are directly opposite the Sun in the sky, and cross the meridian at local midnight.

It is often useful to be able to estimate angles on the sky, and approximate values may be obtained by holding one hand at arm's length. The various angles are shown in the diagram, together with the separations of the various stars in and around Orion.

Meteors

At some time or other, nearly everyone has seen a **meteor** – a 'shooting star' – as it flashed across the sky. The particles that cause meteors – known technically as 'meteoroids' – range in size from that of a grain of sand (or even smaller) to the size of a pea. On any night of the year there are occasional meteors, known as **sporadics**, that may travel in any direction. These occur at a rate that is normally between three and eight in an hour. Far more important, however, are **meteor showers**, which occur at fixed periods of the year, when the Earth encounters a trail of particles left behind by a comet or, very occasionally, by a minor

planet (asteroid). Meteors always appear to diverge from a single point on the sky, known as the **radiant**, and the radiants of major showers are shown on the charts. Meteors that come from a circular area 8° in diameter around the radiant are classed as belonging to the particular shower. All others that do not come from that area are sporadics (or, occasionally from another shower that is active at the same time). A list of the major meteor showers is given on page 31.

Although the positions of the various shower radiants are shown on the charts, looking directly at the radiant is not the most effective way of seeing meteors. They are most likely to be noticed if one is looking about 40–45° away from the radiant position. (This is approximately two hand-spans as shown in the diagram for measuring angles.)

Other objects

Certain other objects may be seen with the naked eye under good conditions. Some were given names in antiquity – Praesepe is one example – but many are known by what are called 'Messier numbers', the numbers in a catalogue of nebulous objects compiled by Charles Messier in the late eighteenth century. Some, such as the Andromeda Galaxy, M31, and the Orion Nebula, M42, may be seen by the naked eye, but all those given in the list will benefit from the use of binoculars.

Meteor shower (showing the Geminids radiant).

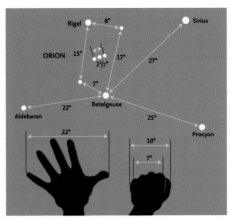

Measuring angles in the sky.

Apart from galaxies, such as M31, which contain thousands of millions of stars, there are also two types of cluster: open clusters, such as M45, the Pleiades, which may consist of a few dozen to some hundreds of stars; and globular clusters, such as Omega Centauri, which are spherical concentrations of many thousands of stars. One or two gaseous nebulae (emission nebulae), consisting of gas illuminated by stars within them, are also visible. The Orion Nebula, M42, is one, and is illuminated by the group of four stars, known as the Trapezium, which may be seen within it by using a good pair of binoculars.

Some interesting objects.

Messier / NGC	Name	Type	Constellation	Maps (months)
—	47 Tucanae	globular cluster	Tucana	All year
—	Hyades	open cluster	Taurus	Oct. – Feb.
—	Melotte 111 (Coma Cluster)	open cluster	Coma Berenices	Mar. – Jun.
M3	—	globular cluster	Canes Venatici	Mar. – Jul.
M4	—	globular cluster	Scorpius	Mar. – Sep.
M8	Lagoon Nebula	gaseous nebula	Sagittarius	Apr. – Oct.
M11	Wild Duck Cluster	open cluster	Scutum	May – Oct.
M13	Hercules Cluster	globular cluster	Hercules	May – Aug.
M15	—	globular cluster	Pegasus	Jul. – Nov.
M20	Trifid Nebula	gaseous nebula	Sagittarius	Apr. – Oct.
M22	—	globular cluster	Sagittarius	Apr. – Oct.
M27	Dumbbell Nebula	planetary nebula	Vulpecula	Jun. – Oct.
M31	Andromeda Galaxy	galaxy	Andromeda	Sep. – Dec.
M35	—	open cluster	Gemini	Nov. – Mar.
M42	Orion Nebula	gaseous nebula	Orion	Oct. – Apr.
M44	Praesepe	open cluster	Cancer	Dec. – Apr.
M45	Pleiades	open cluster	Taurus	Oct. – Feb.
M57	Ring Nebula	planetary nebula	Lyra	Jun. – Sep.
M67	—	open cluster	Cancer	Dec. – May
IC 2602	Southern Pleiades	open cluster	Carina	All year
NGC 2070	Tarantula Nebula	emission nebula	Dorado (LMC)	All year
NGC 3242	Ghost of Jupiter	planetary nebula	Hydra	Jan. – Jun.
NGC 3372	Eta Carinae Nebula	gaseous nebula	Carina	All year
NGC 4755	Jewel Box	open cluster	Crux	All year
NGC 5139	Omega Centauri	globular cluster	Centaurus	Jan. – Sep.

The Southern Circumpolar Constellations

The southern circumpolar constellations are the key to to starting to identify the constellations. For anyone in the southern hemisphere, they are visible at any time of the year, and nearly everyone is familiar with the striking pattern of four stars that make up the constelllation of **Crux** (the Southern Cross), and also the two nearby bright stars **Rigil Kentaurus** and **Hadar** (α and β Centauri respectively). This pattern of stars is visible throughout the year for most observers, although for observers farther north, the stars may become difficult to see, low on the horizon in the southern spring, espcially in the months of October and November.

Crux

The distinctive shape of the constellation of **Crux** is usually easy to identify, although some people (especially northerners unused to the southern sky) may wrongly identify the slightly larger False Cross, formed by the stars **Aspidiske** and **Avior** (ι and ε Carinae respectively) plus **Markeb** and **Alsephina** (κ and δ Velorum). The dark patch of the Coalsack (a dark cloud of obscuring dust) is readily visible on the eastern side of Crux between **Acrux** and **Mimosa** (α and β Crucis).

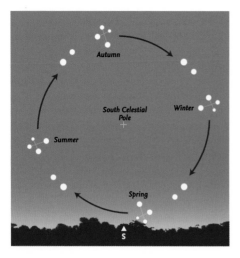

A line through **Gacrux** (γ Crucis) and **Acrux** (α Crucis) points approximately in the direction of the South Celestial Pole, crossing the faint constellations of **Musca** and **Chamaeleon**. Although there is no bright star close to the South Celestial Pole (and even the constellation in which it lies, **Octans**, is faint), an idea of its location helps to identify the region of sky that is always visible. (The altitude of the South Celestial Pole is equal to the observer's latitude south of the equator.) The basic triangular shape of Octans itself is best found by extending a line from **Peacock** (α Pavonis) through β Pavonis, by about the same distance as that between the stars.

Centaurus

Although Crux is a distinctive shape, **Centaurus** is a large, rather straggling constellation, with one notable object, the giant, bright globular cluster **Omega Centauri** (the brightest globular in the sky), which lies towards the north, on the line from **Hadar** (β Centauri) through ε Centauri. Rather than locating the South Celestial Pole from Crux, a better indication is the line, at right angles to the line between Hadar and Rigil Kentaurus that passes across the brightest star in **Circinus** (α).

Carina

Apart from the two stars that form part of the False Cross, the constellation of Carina is, like Centaurus, a large, sprawling constellation. It contains one striking open cluster, the **Southern Pleiades**, and a remarkable emission nebula, the **Eta Carinae Nebula**. The second brightest star in the sky (after Sirius) is **Canopus**, α Carinae, which lies far away to the west.

The Magellanic Clouds

On the opposite side of the South Celestial Pole to Crux and Centaurus lie the two Magellanic Clouds. The **Small Magellanic Cloud** (SMC) lies to one side of the relatively inconspicuous, triangular constellation of **Hydrus**, but is actually within the constellation of **Tucana**.

The stars and constellations inside the circle are always above the horizon, seen from latitude 35°S.

Nearby is another bright globular cluster, **47 Tucanae.** Hydrus itself is also easily identified from the star, **Achernar,** α Eridani, the rather isolated brilliant star at the southern end of **Eridanus,** which wanders a long way south, having begun at the foot of Orion.

The **Large Magellanic Cloud** (LMC) lies within the faint constellation of **Dorado.** Not only is it a large satellite galaxy of the Milky Way Galaxy, but it contains the large, readily visible, **Tarantula Nebula,** an emission nebula that is a major star-forming region.

THE CONSTELLATIONS **11**

The Summer Constellations

The summer sky is dominated by the constellation of **Orion**, with its three 'Belt' stars, as well as by the three bright stars: **Betelgeuse** (α Orionis), **Sirius** (α Canis Majoris), and **Procyon** (α Canis Minoris), which together form the prominent (Southern) 'Summer Triangle'. To the west of Orion is **Taurus**, with orange **Aldebaran** (α Tauri). A line from **Bellatrix** (γ Orionis) through Aldebaran points to the striking **Pleiades** cluster (M45). (The line of three 'Belt' stars indicates the same general path and, in the other direction, points towards Sirius.) A line from **Mintaka** (the westernmost star of the 'Belt') through brilliant **Rigel** (β Orionis) points in the direction of **Achernar** (α Eridani). One from **Alnitak** (at the other end of the 'Belt') through **Saiph** (κ Orionis) indicates the direction of **Canopus** (α Carinae), the second brightest star in the whole sky. A line from Betelgeuse through Sirius points in the general direction of the 'False Cross' in **Vela** and **Carina**.

In the opposite (northern) side of Orion, a line from **Meissa** (λ Orionis) through **Elnath** (β Tauri) leads to **Capella** (α Aurigae), and one from **Betelgeuse** through **Alhena** (γ Geminorum) points to **Pollux** (β Geminorium), the southernmost of the distinctive Castor/Pollux pair. A line across Orion from Bellatrix to Betelgeuse, if extended greatly, indicates the general direction of **Regulus** (α Leonis).

Six of the bright stars that have been mentioned, in different constellations: Capella, Aldebaran, Rigel, Sirius, Procyon and Pollux form what, for northern observers, is sometimes known as the 'Winter Hexagon'. Pollux is accompanied to the northwest by the slightly fainter star of **Castor** (α Geminorum), the second 'Twin'.

Several of the stars in this region of the sky show distinctive tints: Betelgeuse (α Orionis) is reddish, Aldebaran (α Tauri) is orange and Rigel (α Orionis) is blue-white.

The Autumn Constellations

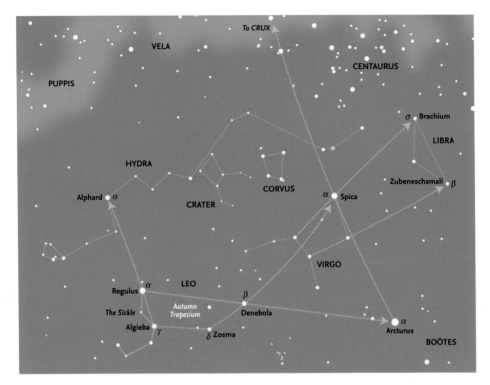

During the autumn season, the principal constellation is the zodiacal constellation of **Leo**, whose principal star **Regulus** (α Leonis) is one of the five bright stars that may occasionally be occulted by the Moon. Regulus forms the 'dot' of the upside-down 'question mark' of stars, known as the 'Sickle'. The body of Leo itself is sometimes known as the 'Trapezium' (here, the 'Autumn Trapezium'), and its sides may be used to find other objects in the sky.

A line extended from **Algieba** (γ Leonis), the second star in the 'Sickle', through Regulus points to **Alphard** (α Hydrae) the brightest star in **Hydra**, the largest of the 88 constellations, which sprawls a long way across the sky from its distinctively shaped 'head' of stars, southwest of Regulus. A line from Regulus through **Denebola** (β Leonis) at the other end of the constellation of Leo points towards **Arcturus** (α Boötis), the brightest star in the

northern hemisphere of the sky. Another line, down the 'back' of Leo, from **Zosma** (δ Leonis) through Denebola points in the general direction of **Spica** (α Virginis) the principal star in the constellation of **Virgo**.

Although Spica is the brightest star in the zodiacal constellation of Virgo, the remainder of the constellation is not remarkable, consisting of a rough quadrilateral of stars with fainter lines extending outwards. The two sides of the main quadrilateral, if extended, point eastwards towards the two principal stars, **Zubeneschamali** and **Brachium** (β and σ Librae, respectively), of the small zodiacal constellation of **Libra**. The two small constellations of **Corvus** and **Crater** lie between Virgo and the long stretch of Hydra. A line from Arcturus through Spica, if extended far to the south across the sky, points to the distinctive constellation of **Crux**.

The Winter Constellations

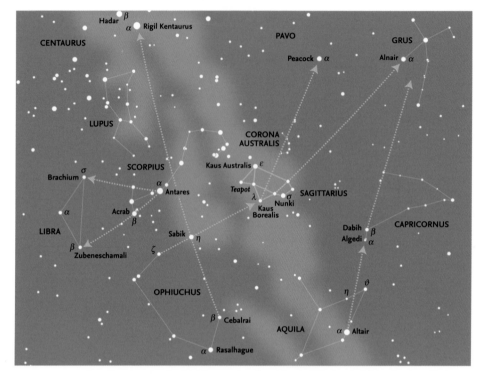

During the winter season, the Milky Way runs right across the sky, and the distinctive constellation of **Scorpius** is clearly visible, with bright red **Antares** (α Scorpii) and the 'sting', trailing behind the star to the west. Scorpius used to be a much larger constellation until the small zodiacal constellation of **Libra** was formed from some of its stars. The two sides of the 'fan' of stars immediately east of Antares, if extended, point to the two principal stars of Libra, **Zubeneschamali** and **Brachium** (β and σ Librae, respectively) on the southern and northern sides of the constellation.

North of Scorpius lies the large constellation of **Ophiuchus**. The ecliptic runs through the southern portion of Ophiuchus, and the Sun spends far more time in that constellation than it does in neighbouring Scorpius. A line from **Cebalrai** (β Ophiuchi) in the north of the constellation, through **Sabik** (η Ophiuchi), if extended right across

Scorpius, carries you to the two bright stars of **Centaurus**, **Rigil Kentaurus** and **Hadar** (α and β Centauri, respectively). Between Libra and Centaurus lies the straggling constellation of **Lupus** with no distinct pattern of stars.

A line from the fainter star ζ Ophiuchi through **Sabik** points towards **Kaus Borealis** (λ Sagittarii) the 'lid' of the 'Teapot' of **Sagittarius**. From there two lines radiate (on the west) across **Corona Australis** towards **Peacock** (α Pavonis) and (on the east) **Alnair** (α Guis) in the small constellation of **Grus**.

Also north of **Scorpius** is the constellation of **Aquila**, with its brightest star, **Altair** (α Aquilae). The diamond shape of the 'wings' of Aquila may be used to locate **Algedi** (α Capricorni), a prominent double star in **Capricornus**. A line through **Dabih** (β Capricorni) and the western side of that basically triangular constellation, when extended, also points in the direction of the constellation of **Grus**.

The Spring Constellations

In spring, the constellation of **Pegasus** and the Great Square of Pegasus are prominent in the north. One star in the Square, **Alpheratz**, at the northwestern corner, actually belongs to the neighbouring constellation of **Andromeda**. A diagonal line across the Square from Alpheratz (α Andromedae) through **Markab** (α Pegasi) points to **Sadalmelik** (α Aquarii), just to the west of the 'Y-shaped' asterism of the 'Water Jar' in the zodiacal constellation of **Aquarius**. Further extended, that line carries you to the centre of the triangular constellation of **Capricornus**.

The constellation of **Pisces** consists of two lines of stars running to the south and east of the Great Square. In mythological representations, the two fish are linked by ribbons, tied together at **Alrescha** (α Piscium). The distinctive asterism of **The Circlet** lies at the western end of the southern line of stars. The two north-south lines of the Great Square may be used as guides to other constellations. The western line from **Scheat** (β Pegasi) through Markab, if extended about three times, crosses Aquarius and points to the bright, fairly isolated star, **Fomalhaut** (α Piscis Austrini) in the constellation of **Piscis Austrinus** and then onward to **Tiaki** (β Gruis) in the centre of cross of stars within **Grus**. The eastern line, from Alpheratz through **Algenib** (γ Pegasi), extended about three-and-a-half times, indicates **Ankaa** (α Phoenicis) in the constellation of **Phoenix**.

The line between Markab and Algenib may be extended as an arc to lead to **Menkar** (α Ceti) in the 'tail' of Cetus. A line from Menkar through **Diphda** (β Ceti) also points to Fomalhaut in Piscis Austrinus. Diphda and Fomalhaut form the base of an almost perfect, large isoceles triangle, with **Achernar** (α Eridani) at the other apex. **Eridanus** itself is a long, trailing constellation that begins far to the north, near **Rigel** in **Orion**.

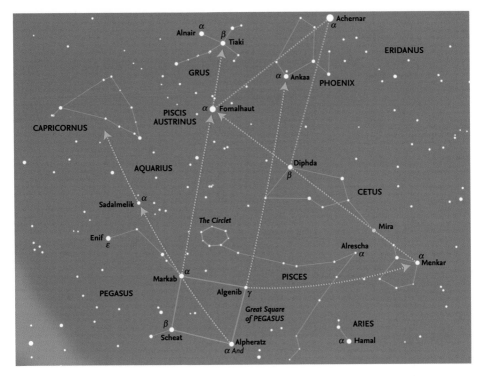

The Moon

The monthly pages include diagrams showing the phase of the Moon for every day of the month, and also indicate the day in the **lunation** (or **age** of the Moon), which begins at New Moon. Although the main features of the surface – the light highlands and the dark maria (seas) – may be seen with the naked eye, far more features may be detected with the use of binoculars or any telescope. The many craters are best seen when they are close to the **terminator** (the boundary between the illuminated and the non-illuminated areas of the surface), when the Sun rises or sets over any particular region of the Moon and the crater walls or central peaks cast strong shadows. Most features become difficult to see at Full Moon, although this is the best time to see the bright ray systems surrounding certain craters. Accompanying the Moon map on the following pages is a list of prominent features, including the days in the lunation when features are normally close to the terminator and thus easiest to see. A few bright features such as Linné and Proclus, visible when well illuminated, are also listed. One feature, Rupes Recta (the Straight Wall) is readily visible only when it casts a shadow with light from the east, appearing as a light line when illuminated from the opposite direction.

The dates of visibility vary slightly through the effects of **libration**. Because the Moon's orbit is inclined to the Earth's equator and also because it moves in an ellipse, the Moon appears to rock slightly from side to side (and nod up and down). Features near the **limb** (the edge of the Moon) may vary considerably in their location and visibility. (This is easily noticeable with Mare Crisium and the craters Tycho and Plato.) Another effect is that at crescent phases before and after New Moon, the normally non-illuminated portion of the Moon receives a certain amount of light, reflected from the Earth. This **Earthshine** may enable certain bright features (such as Aristarchus, Kepler and Copernicus) to be detected even though they are not illuminated by sunlight.

The Moon phases. *During its orbit around the Earth we see different portions of the illuminated side of the Moon's surface.*

The Moon at First Quarter (south is up).

Map of the Moon

SOUTH

Abulfeda	6:20
Agrippa	7:21
Albategnius	7:21
Aliacensis	7:21
Alphonsus	8:22
Anaxagoras	9:23
Anaximenes	11:25
Archimedes	8:22
Aristarchus	11:25
Aristillus	7:21
Aristoteles	6:20
Arzachel	8:22
Atlas	4:18
Autolycus	7:21
Barrow	7:21
Billy	12:26
Birt	8:22
Blancanus	9:23
Bullialdus	9:23
Bürg	5:19
Campanus	10:24
Cassini	7:21
Catharina	6:20
Clavius	9:23
Cleomedes	3:17
Copernicus	9:23
Cyrillus	6:20
Delambre	6:20
Deslandres	8:22
Endymion	3:17
Eratosthenes	8:22
Eudoxus	6:20
Fra Mauro	9:23
Fracastorius	5:19
Franklin	4:18
Gassendi	11:25
Geminus	3:17
Goclenius	4:18
Grimaldi	13-14:27-28
Gutenberg	5:19
Hercules	5:19
Herodotus	11:25
Hipparchus	7:21
Hommel	5:19
Humboldt	3:15
Janssen	4:18
Julius Caesar	6:20
Kepler	10:24
Landsberg	10:24
Langrenus	3:17
Letronne	11:25
Linné	6
Longomontanus	9:23

The numbers indicate the age of the Moon when features are usually best visible.

NORTH

18

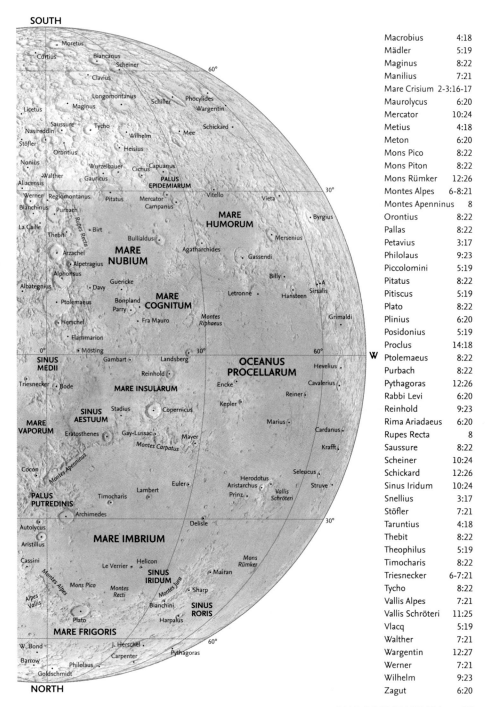

SOUTH

Moretus, Curtius, Blancanus, Scheiner, Clavius, Longomontanus, Schiller, Phocylides, Wargentin, Licetus, Maginus, Nasireddin, Saussure, Tycho, Wilhelm, Mee, Schickard, Stöfler, Heisius, Orontius, Nonius, Wurzelbauer, Cichus, Capuanus, Walther, Gauricus, PALUS EPIDEMIARUM, Aliacensis, Werner, Regiomontanus, Pitatus, Mercator, Vitello, Vieta, Blanchinus, Purbach, Campanus, La Caille, Thebit, Birt, Bullialdus, MARE HUMORUM, Byrgius, Arzachel, MARE NUBIUM, Agatharchides, Mersenius, Alpetragius, Gassendi, Alphonsus, Billy, Albategnius, Davy, Guericke, Sirsalis, Ptolemaeus, Bonpland, MARE COGNITUM, Letronne, Hansteen, Parry, Herschel, Fra Mauro, Montes Riphaeus, Grimaldi, Flammarion, Mösting, SINUS MEDII, Gambart, Landsberg, OCEANUS PROCELLARUM, Hevelius, Triesnecker, Bode, Reinhold, Cavalerius, MARE INSULARUM, Encke, Reiner, Kepler, MARE VAPORUM, SINUS AESTUUM, Stadius, Copernicus, Marius, Eratosthenes, Gay-Lussac, Mayer, Cardanus, Montes Carpatus, Krafft, Cocon, Herodotus, Seleucus, PALUS PUTREDINIS, Lambert, Euler, Aristarchus, Struve, Timocharis, Prinz, Vallis Schröteri, Archimedes, Delisle, Autolycus, MARE IMBRIUM, Aristillus, Cassini, Helicon, Mons Rümker, Le Verrier, SINUS IRIDUM, Mairan, Mons Pico, Montes Recti, Sharp, Alpes Vallis, Bianchini, SINUS RORIS, Plato, Harpalus, MARE FRIGORIS, W. Bond, J. Herschel, Barrow, Carpenter, Pythagoras, Philolaus, Goldschmidt

60°, 30°, 0°, 30°, 60°

W

NORTH

MAP OF THE MOON **19**

Eclipses in 2022

Lunar eclipses

There are two lunar eclipses in 2022, on May 16 and November 8. Both are total. The first eclipse will be completely visible (both penumbral and umbral phases) from the whole of South America. The maximum (total) phases are visible for much of North America, although the Moon will be low in the sky. West Africa will see the Moon enter the **umbra** before Moonset. The second lunar eclipse is visible primarily from the region of the Pacific Ocean. Early phases are visible from North America, but only the West Coast will see maximum eclipse come to an end before the Moon sets.

Solar eclipses

There are two partial solar eclipses in 2022. Neither are particularly striking. In the first, on April 30, 64 per cent of the Sun will be covered, with the event visible from Chile and Argentina. The second partial eclipse, on October 25, when a maximum 86 per cent of the Sun will be covered, will be visible over a wide area of Asia and Europe. The percentage of the Sun covered will be about 60 per cent in Moscow, 40 per cent in Berlin, and just 20 per cent in London.

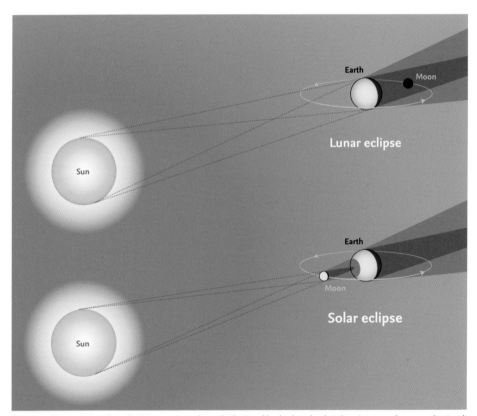

A lunar eclipse occurs when the Moon passes through the Earth's shadow (top). When it passes between the Earth and the Sun (bottom) there is a solar eclipse.

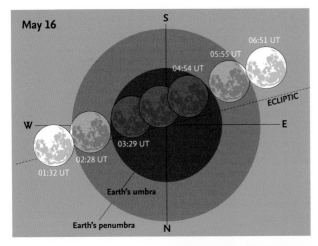

May 16

06:51 UT
05:55 UT
04:54 UT
03:29 UT
02:28 UT
01:32 UT

ECLIPTIC

S

W   E

N

Earth's umbra

Earth's penumbra

The total lunar eclipse of May 16 will be visible in its entirety from South America. Central Africa will see the Moon enter the umbra, as will western Europe, where the Moon will be low. In the United States, the total and later penumbral phases will be visible.

The lunar eclipse of November 8 is total, but mainly visible from the Pacific region. The end of the eclipse will be visible from Australia, particularly eastern Australia. The Midwest of North America will see the beginning of totality, with the end visible from the West Coast.

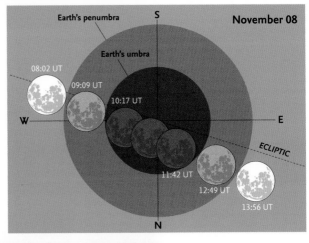

Earth's penumbra

November 08

S

Earth's umbra

08:02 UT
09:09 UT
10:17 UT

W   E

ECLIPTIC

11:42 UT
12:49 UT
13:56 UT

N

A sequence of five images of the Moon, taken by Akira Fuji, showing the progression of the Moon (from left to right: west to east) through the Earth's shadow.

The Planets in 2022

Mercury and Venus

Although **Venus** may be prominent in the sky for many months at a time, the innermost planet, **Mercury**, is readily visible only at certain elongations. Not every one is favourable. In 2022, for example, Mercury comes to greatest elongation seven times, but it is most visible at six of those only. These occasions are shown on the diagrams below.

Venus is prominent throughout 2022, but has a single greatest elongation on March 20, shown on the top-right diagram on this page.

The path of Mars in 2022. Mars comes to opposition on December 8 (south is up).

Mars

Because its orbit lies outside that of the Earth, so it takes longer to complete a full orbit, **Mars** does not come to opposition every year. Instead, it remains in the sky for many months at a time, moving slowly along the ecliptic. It does come to opposition in 2022, and the planet's path is shown on the large chart here. It begins the year in **Scorpius** at magnitude 1.5. It moves right across the sky, slowly brightening to mag. -1.9 at opposition on December 8 in **Taurus**, and fading to mag. -1.2 by the end of the year. Oppositions occur during a period of **retrograde motion**, when the planet appears to move westwards against the pattern of distant stars. As mentioned, there was no opposition in 2021. The planet begins to retrograde on 31 October 2022 and remains retrograding to the end of the year.

Because of its eccentric orbit, which carries it at very differing distances from the Sun (and Earth), not all oppositions of Mars are equally favourable for observation. The relative positions of Mars and the Earth are shown here. It will be seen that the opposition of 2018 was very close and thus favourable for observation, and that of 2020 was also reasonably good. By comparison, opposition in 2027 will be at a far greater distance, so the planet will appear much smaller.

Mars came to opposition on 13 October 2020. This image was obtained by Damian Peach with a 14-inch Celestron telescope on September 30, when Mars was magnitude -2.5. South is at the top.

The oppositions of Mars between 2018 and 2033. In 2022, Mars comes to opposition on December 8.

The path of Jupiter in 2022. Jupiter comes to opposition on September 26. Background stars are shown down to magnitude 6.5. South is up on all maps.

Jupiter and Saturn

In 2022, **Jupiter** and **Saturn** are in neighbouring constellations. Jupiter moves across **Aquarius**, into **Pisces** and then just into **Cetus**, where it begins to retrograde on July 29. It comes to opposition, within Pisces, on September 26, and resumes direct motion on November 26. Saturn, by contrast, remains within one constellation, **Capricornus**, retrograding from June 6 to October 23, with opposition on August 14.

Jupiter's four large satellites are readily visible in binoculars. Not all four are visible all the time, sometimes hidden behind the planet or invisible in front of it. **Io**, the closest to Jupiter, orbits in just under 1.8 days, and Callisto, the farthest away, takes about 16.7 days. In between are **Europa** (c. 3.6 days) and **Ganymede**, the largest, (c. 7.1 days). The diagram shows the satellites' motions around the time of opposition.

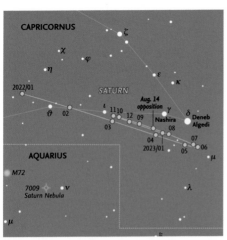

The path of Saturn in 2022. Saturn comes to opposition on August 14. Background stars are shown down to magnitude 6.5.

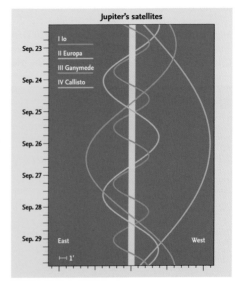

Uranus and Neptune

Uranus is in **Aries** for the whole year. Initially retrograding (at mag. 5.7), it resumes direct motion on January 22. It begins its retrograde motion on August 25. It reaches opposition (mag. 5.6) on November 9 (just after Full Moon, so observation will be difficult). It is still retrograding at the end of the year, when it is again mag. 5.7.

Neptune is in **Aquarius** for most of 2022, making an excursion into **Pisces** between May and August. Initially at mag. 7.9, it moves eastwards until June 29, when it begins to retrograde. It comes to opposition (at mag. 7.8) on September 16 (just before Last Quarter). It resumes direct motion on December 4, and ends the year at mag. 7.9.

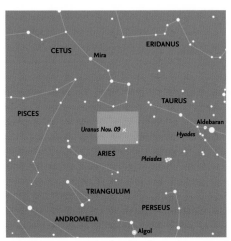

In 2022, Uranus may be found in the southern part of the constellation of Aries.

The path of Uranus in 2022. Uranus comes to opposition on November 9. All stars brighter than magnitude 7.5 are shown.

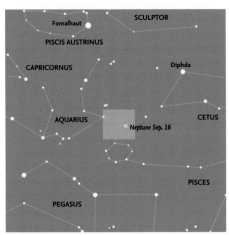

In 2022, Neptune is to be found near the boundary between Aquarius and Pisces. It comes to opposition on September 16.

The path of Neptune in 2022. The planet moves from Aquarius into Pisces on May 1, and back into Aquarius on August 19. All stars brighter than magnitude 8.5 are shown.

Minor Planets in 2022

Several minor planets rise above magnitude 9 in 2022, but just three come to opposition. These are **(7) Iris** in **Gemini** on January 13; **(4) Vesta** in **Aquarius** on August 22; and **(3) Juno** also in **Aquarius** on September 7. The dwarf planet **(1) Ceres** is bright the whole year, reaching mag. 8.3 on December 31. **(4) Vesta** is also bright the whole year, and **(2) Pallas** is bright from early September. **(3)** Juno rises above mag. 9.0 in late July, before opposition, and fades below mag. 9.0 in early November.

The path of the minor planet (7) Iris around its opposition on January 13 (mag. 7.6). Background stars are shown down to magnitude 9.0 (south is up).

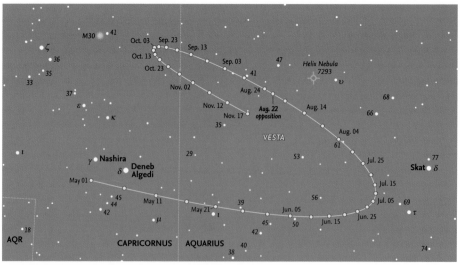

The path of the minor planet (4) Vesta around its opposition on August 22 (mag. 5.8). Background stars are shown down to magnitude 7.5 (south is up).

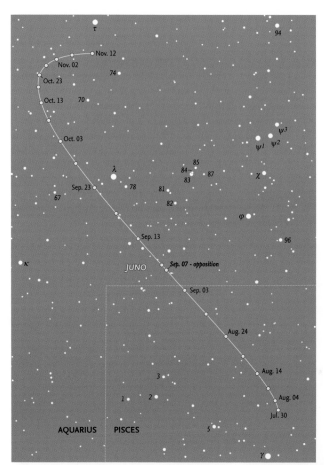

The path of the minor planet (3) Juno around its opposition on September 7 (mag. 7.9). Background stars are shown down to magnitude 9.0 (south is up).

The three charts below show the areas covered by the larger maps on these pages, in a lighter blue. The white cross shows the position of the minor planet at the day of its opposition (south is up on all maps).

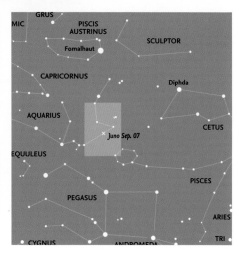

Comets in 2022

Although comets may occasionally become very striking objects in the sky, as was the case with Comet C/2020 F3 NEOWISE in 2020, their occurrence and particularly the existence or length of any tail and their overall magnitude are notoriously difficult to predict. Naturally, it is only possible to predict the return of periodic comets (whose names have the prefix 'P'). Many comets appear unexpectedly (these have names with the prefix 'C'). Bright, readily visible comets such as C/1995 Y1 Hyakutake, C/1995 O1 Hale-Bopp, C/2006 P1 McNaught or C/2020 F3 NEOWISE are rare. Most periodic comets are faint and only a very small number, such as comet C/2020 M3 (ATLAS), become bright enough to be easily visible with the naked eye or with binoculars.

The comet most likely to become visible in 2022 is C/2017 K2 (PanSTARRS) which may become magnitude 9 in March and could reach magnitude 6 in June to August. Comets 19P/Borrelly and 67P/Churyumov-Gerasimenko may be faintly visible (but fading) early in the year.

The Comet C/2020 F3 NEOWISE photographed by Nick James on 17 July 2020, showing the light-coloured dust tail, together with the blue ion tail.

The path of comet C/2017 K2 (PanSTARRS) in 2022. Background stars are shown down to magnitude 6.5 (south is up).

Introduction to the Month-by-Month Guide

The monthly charts

The pages devoted to each month contain a pair of charts showing the appearance of the night sky, looking south and looking north. The charts (as with all the charts in this book) are drawn for the latitude of 35°S, so observers farther north will see slightly more of the sky on the northern horizon, and slightly less on the southern, with corresponding changes if they are farther south. The horizon areas are, of course, those most likely to be affected by poor observing conditions caused by haze, mist or smoke. In addition, stars close to the horizon are always dimmed by atmospheric absorption, so sometimes the faintest stars marked on the charts may not be visible.

The three times shown for each chart require a little explanation. The charts are drawn to show the appearance at 11 p.m. for the 1st of each month. The same appearance will apply an hour earlier (10 p.m.) on the 15th, and yet another hour earlier (9 p.m.) at the end of the month (shown as the 1st of the following month). Daylight Saving Time (DST) is not used in South Africa. In New Zealand, it applies from the last Sunday of September to the first Sunday of April. In those Australian states with DST, it runs from the first Sunday in October to the first Sunday in April. The appropriate times are shown on the monthly charts. Times of specific events are shown on the 24-hour clock of Universal Time (UT), used by astronomers worldwide, and corrections for the local time zone (and DST where employed) may be found from the details inside the front cover.

The charts may be used for earlier or later times during the night. To observe two hours earlier, use the charts for the preceding month; for two hours later, the charts for the next month.

Meteors

Details of specific meteor showers are given in the months when they come to maximum,

regardless of whether they begin or end in other months. Note that not all the respective radiants are marked on the charts for that particular month, because the radiants may be below the horizon, or lie in constellations that are not readily visible during the month of maximum. For this reason, special charts for the Eta (η) Aquariids (May), the Alpha (α) Aurigids (August and September) and the Leonids (November) are given here. As just explained, however, meteors from such showers may still be seen, because the most effective region for seeing meteors is some 40–45° away from the radiant, and that area of sky may well be above the horizon. A table of the best meteor showers visible during the year is also given here. The rates given are based on the properties of the meteor streams, and are those that an experienced observer might see under ideal conditions. Generally, the observed rates will be far less.

Shower	Dates of activity 2022	Date of maximum 2022	Possible hourly rate
α-Centaurids	January 31 to February 20	February 8	6
γ-Normids	February 25 to March 28	March 14–15	6
π-Puppids	April 15 to April 28	April 23–24	var.
η-Aquariids	April 19 to May 28	May 6	50
α-Capricornids	July 3 to August 15	July 30	5
Southern δ-Aquariids	July 12 to August 23	July 30	25
Piscis Austrinids	July 15 to August 10	July 28	5
Perseids	July 17 to August 24	August 12–13	100
α-Aurigids	August 28 to September 5	September 1	6
Southern Taurids	September 10 to November 20	October 10–11	5
Orionids	October 2 to November 7	October 21–22	20
Northern Taurids	October 20 to December 10	November 12–13	5
Leonids	November 6 to November 30	November 17–18	10
Phoenicids	November 28 to December 9	December 2	var.
Puppid Velids	December 1 to December 15	December 7	10
Geminids	December 4 to December 20	December 14–15	150

Meteors that are brighter than magnitude -4 (approximately the maximum magnitude reached by Venus) are known as *fireballs* or *bolides*.

The photographs

As an aid to identification – especially as some people find it difficult to relate charts to the actual stars they see in the sky – one or more photographs of constellations visible in certain specific months are included. It should be noted, however, that because of the limitations of the photographic and printing processes, and the differences between the sensitivity of different individuals to faint starlight (especially in their ability to detect different colours), and the degree to which they have become adapted to the dark, the apparent brightness of stars in the photographs will not necessarily precisely match that seen by any one observer.

The Moon calendar

The Moon calendar is largely self-explanatory. It shows the phase of the Moon for every day of the month, with the exact times (in Universal Time) of New Moon, First Quarter, Full Moon and Last Quarter. Because the times are calculated from the Moon's actual orbital parameters, some of the times shown will, naturally, fall during daylight, but any difference is too small to affect the appearance of the Moon on that date. Also shown is the *age* of the Moon (the day in the *lunation*), beginning at New Moon, which may be used to determine the best time for observation of specific lunar features.

The Moon

The section on the Moon includes details of any lunar or solar eclipses that may occur during the month (visible from anywhere on Earth). Similar information is given about any important occultations. Mainly, however, this section summarizes when the Moon passes close to planets or the five prominent stars close to the ecliptic. The dates when the Moon is closest to the Earth (at *perigee*) and farthest from it (at *apogee*) are shown in the monthly calendars, and only mentioned here when they are particularly significant, such as the nearest and farthest during the year

The planets and minor planets

Brief details are given of the location, movement and brightness of the planets from Mercury to Saturn throughout the month. None of the planets can, of course, be seen when they are close to the Sun, so such periods are generally noted. All of the planets may sometimes lie on the opposite side of the Sun to the Earth (at superior conjunction), but in the case of the inferior planets, Mercury and Venus, they may also pass between the Earth and the Sun (at inferior conjunction)

A fireball (with flares approximately as bright as the Full Moon), photographed against a weak auroral display by D. Buczynski from Tarbat Ness in Scotland on 22 January 2017.

and are normally invisible for a longer or shorter period of time. Those two planets are normally easiest to see around either eastern or western elongation, in the evening or morning sky, respectively. Not every elongation is favourable, so although every elongation is listed, only those where observing conditions are favourable are shown in the individual diagrams of events.

The dates at which the superior planets reverse their motion (from direct motion to retrograde, and retrograde to direct) and of opposition (when a planet generally reaches its maximum brightness) are given. Some planets, especially distant Saturn, may spend most or all of the year in a single constellation. Jupiter and Saturn are normally easiest to see around opposition, which occurs every year. Mars, by contrast, moves relatively rapidly against the background stars and in some years never comes to opposition. In 2020, Jupiter and Saturn are close together in the sky throughout the year, so a special chart is shown on page 24.

Uranus is normally magnitude 5.7–5.9, and thus at the limit of naked-eye visibility under exceptionally dark skies, but bright enough to be readily visible in binoculars. Because its orbital period is so long (over 84 years), Uranus moves only slowly along the ecliptic, and often remains within a single constellation for a whole year. The chart on page 25 shows its position during 2022.

Similar considerations apply to Neptune, although it is always fainter (generally magnitude 7.8–8.0), still visible in most binoculars. It takes about 164.8 years to complete one orbit of the Sun. As with Uranus, it frequently spends a complete year in one constellation. Its chart is also on page 25.

In any year, few minor planets ever become bright enough to be detectable in binoculars. Just one, (4) Vesta, on rare occasions brightens sufficiently for it to be visible to the naked eye. Our limit for visibility is magnitude 9.0 and details and charts are given for those objects that exceed that magnitude during the year, normally around opposition. To assist in recognition of a planet or minor planet as it moves against the background stars, the latter are shown to a fainter magnitude than the object at opposition. Minor-planet charts for 2022 are on pages 26 and 27.

The ecliptic charts

Although the ecliptic charts are primarily designed to show the positions and motions of the major planets, they also show the motion of the Sun during the month. The light-tinted area shows the area of the sky that is invisible during daylight, but the darker area gives an indication of which constellations are likely to be visible at some time of the night. The closer a planet is to the border between dark and light, the more difficult it will be to see in the twilight.

The monthly calendar

For each month, a calendar shows details of significant events, including when planets are close to one another in the sky, close to the Moon, or close to any one of five bright stars that are spaced along the ecliptic. The times shown are given in Universal Time (UT), always used by astronomers throughout the year, and which is identical to Greenwich Mean Time (GMT). So during the summer months, they do not show Summer Time, which will need to be taken for the observing location.

The diagrams of interesting events

Each month, a number of diagrams show the appearance of the sky when certain events take place. However, the exact positions of celestial objects and their separations greatly depend on the observer's position on Earth. When the Moon is one of the objects involved, because it is relatively close to Earth, there may be very significant changes from one location to another. Close approaches between planets or between a planet and a star are less affected by changes of location, which may thus be ignored.

The diagrams showing the appearance of the sky are drawn at latitude 35°S and longitude 150°E (approximately that of Sydney, Australia), so will be approximately correct for much of Australia. However, for an observer farther north (say, Brisbane or Darwin), a planet or star listed as being north of the Moon will appear even farther north, whereas one south of the Moon will appear closer to it – or may even be hidden (occulted) by it. For an observer at a latitude greater than 35°S (such as in New Zealand), there will be corresponding changes in the opposite direction: for a star or planet south of the Moon, the separation will increase, and for one north of the Moon, the separation will decrease. This is particularly important when occultations occur, which may be visible from one location, but not another. However, there are no major occultations visible in 2022.

Ideally, details should be calculated for each individual observer, but this is obviously impractical. In fact, positions and separations are actually calculated for a theoretical observer located at the centre of the Earth.

So the details given regarding the positions of the various bodies should be used as a guide to their location. A similar situation arises with the times that are shown. These are calculated according to certain technical criteria, which need not concern us here. However, they do not necessarily indicate the exact time when two bodies are closest together. Similarly, dates and times are given, even if they fall in daylight, when the objects are likely to be completely invisible. However, such times do give an indication that the objects concerned will be in the same general area of the sky during both the preceding and the following nights.

Data used in this Guide

The data given in this Guide, such as timings and distances between objects, have been computed with a program developed by the US Naval Observatory in Washington D.C., widely regarded as the most accurate computation. As such, the data may differ slightly from information given elsewhere.

Key to the symbols used on the monthy star maps.

ECLIPTIC

PISCES

AQUARIUS

SCULPTOR

Mira ⊙

CETUS

Fomalhaut

PISCIS
AUSTRINUS

FORNAX

PHOENIX

GRUS

INDUS

ERIDANUS

HOROLOGIUM

Achernar

TUCANA

RETICULUM

SMC

LEPUS

CAELUM

SiC

47 Tucanae

HYDRUS

PEACOCK

Peacock

ZENITH

COLUMBA

DORADO

LMC

MENSA

South Celestial
Pole

OCTANS

PAVO

Adhara

Canopus

PICTOR

Tarantula
Nebula

CHAMAELEON

APUS

Sirius

CARINA

VOLANS

TRIANGULUM
AUSTRALE

CANIS MAJOR

PUPPIS

Southern
Pleiades

MUSCA

S

ARA

Eta Carinae Nebula

Acrux

Coalsack

Hadar

CIRCINUS

Rigil
Kentaurus

False Cross

CRUX

Jewel Box

LUPUS

VELA

Mimosa

PYXIS

CENTAURUS

ANTLIA

Omega
Centauri

HYDRA

Alphard

Ghost of Jupiter

CANCER

HYDRA

CORVUS

CENTAURUS

SEXTANS

CRATER

Regulus

ECLIPTIC

E

W

N

January 01   11 p.m.   (12 p.m. DST)
January 15   10 p.m.   (11 p.m. DST)
February 01   9 p.m.   (10 p.m. DST)

January – Looking South

January – Looking South

Crux is now quite prominent as it rises in the east, and even **Rigil Kentaurus** and **Hadar** (α and β Centauri), although low, are becoming easier to see. The whole of **Carina** is visible, with both the **Eta Carinae Nebula** and the **Southern Pleiades** between Crux and the **False Cross** of stars from the constellations of Carina and **Vela**. **Canopus** (α Carinae) is high in the south, roughly three-quarters of the way from the horizon to the zenith. Also in the south, but slightly lower, is the **Large Magellanic Cloud** (LMC). **Achernar** (α Eridani) is prominent between the constellations of **Hydrus** and **Phoenix**. The **Small Magellanic Cloud** (SMC) and **47 Tucanae** are well-placed for observation alongside Hydrus. **Fomalhaut** (α Piscis Austrini) may be glimpsed low on the horizon towards the west as may **Peacock** (α Pavonis) farther towards the south. The whole of **Pavo** and **Grus** is visible, together with most of **Indus.**

Meteors

The year does not start well for southern meteor observers. The **α-Centaurids** (active late January to February) have low maximum rates, as do the **γ-Normids** (February to March). Only with the **π-Puppids** (maximum April 23–24) is there any likelihood of a higher rate of about 40, although even that is rare. The **Southern δ-Aquarids** (maximum July 30) have a rate of about 20 per hour, as do the **Orionids** (October 21). The **Leonids** (maximum November 17–18) have a rate of 10 per hour. The **Phoenicids** in November–December (maximum December 2) are unpredictable, but may show strong activity. The last major shower of the year, the **Geminids** (maximum December 14) finally achieves a rate of about 120 per hour.

Part of the southern Milky Way. The two bright stars near the bottom of the image are α and β Centauri. The constellation of Crux is near the centre. The Eta Carinae Nebula and the Southern Pleiades are near the top-right corner.

HYDRA

CRATER

SEXTANS

ANTLIA

LEO

Ghost of Jupiter

VELA

PYXIS

Regulus

HYDRA

Alphard

Algieba

CARINA

PUPPIS

MONOCEROS

M67

M44 Praesepe

CANCER

Canopus

COLUMBA

CANIS MAJOR

Procyon

CANIS MINOR

Pollux

Castor

Adhara

Alhena

GEMINI

LYNX

ZENITH

Sirius

Betelgeuse

M35

CAELUM

M42
Orion Nebula

AURIGA

DORADO

LEPUS

Rigel

ORION

Elnath

N

Aldebaran

Capella

Hyades

The
Kids

ERIDANUS

TAURUS

PERSEUS

FORNAX

Pleiades

Algol

ECLIPTIC

PHOENIX

ARIES

Mira

TRIANGULUM

SCULPTOR

CETUS

Hamal

PISCES

W

January 01   11 p.m.   (12 p.m. DST)
January 15   10 p.m.   (11 p.m. DST)

January – Looking North

The northern sky is dominated by **Orion**, prominent during the summer months and visible at some time during the night. It is highly distinctive, with a line of three stars that form the 'Belt'. To most observers, the bright star **Betelgeuse** (α Orionis), shows a reddish tinge, in contrast to the brilliant bluish-white **Rigel** (β Orionis). The three stars of the belt lie directly south of the celestial equator. A vertical line of three 'stars' forms the 'Sword' that hangs south of the Belt. With good viewing, the central 'star' appears as a hazy spot, even to the naked eye, and is actually the **Orion Nebula.** Binoculars reveal the four stars of the Trapezium, which illuminate the nebula.

Orion's Belt points down to the northwest towards **Taurus** (the Bull) and orange-tinted **Aldebaran** (α Tauri). Close to Aldebaran, there is a conspicuous 'V' of stars, called the **Hyades** cluster. (Despite appearances, Aldebaran is not part of the cluster.) Farther along, the same line from Orion passes above a bright cluster of stars, the **Pleiades,** or Seven Sisters. Even the smallest pair of binoculars reveals this as a beautiful group of bluish-white stars. The two most conspicuous of the other stars in Taurus lie directly below Orion, and form an elongated triangle with Aldebaran. The northernmost, **Elnath** (β Tauri), was once considered to be part of the constellation of **Auriga.**

The constellation of Orion dominates the northern sky during this period of the year, and is a useful starting point for recognizing other constellations in the area (see page 36). Here, orange Betelgeuse, blue-white Rigel and the pinkish Orion Nebula are prominent (south is up).

The Moon's phases for January

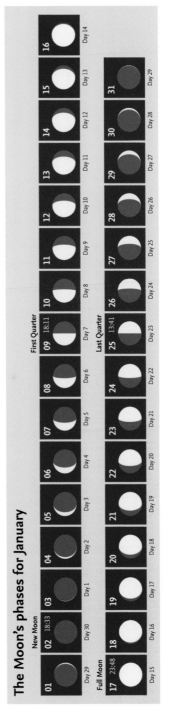

January – Moon and Planets

The Earth

The Earth reaches perihelion (the closest point to the Sun in its yearly orbit) on January 4 at 06:55 Universal Time, when its distance is 0.983336540 AU (147,105,052.565 km).

The Moon

On January 3, the Moon passes 7.5° south of **Venus** and on January 4, 3.1° south of **Mercury**, followed, later that day, 4.2° south of **Saturn**. The first of these events is very close to the Sun and difficult to see. On January 6, the Moon, a waxing crescent in the evening sky, is 4.5° south of **Jupiter** in **Aquarius**. On January 11, two days after First Quarter, the Moon passes 1.5° south of **Uranus** in **Aries**. On January 14, waxing gibbous, three days before Full Moon, it is 6° north of **Aldebaran** in **Taurus**. On January 17

(Full Moon), it is 2.6° south of **Pollux**. By January 20, it is in **Leo**, passing 4.9° north of **Regulus** and between it and **Algieba**. On January 24, the Moon is 5.5° north of **Spica**, and on January 27 it passes 3.7° north of Antares. Two days later (January 29) it is 2.4° south of **Mars**.

The planets

Mercury and **Venus** are close to the Sun and largely lost in twilight. **Mars** at mag. 1.4, initially in **Ophiuchus**, moves into **Sagittarius** and is difficult to see in the morning twilight. **Jupiter** is visible in the morning sky in **Aquarius** at mag. -2.1. **Saturn** is in **Capricornus** and too close to the Sun to be easily visible. **Uranus** is mag. 5.7 in **Aries**, resuming direct motion on January 22, and **Neptune** is mag. 7.9 in **Pisces**. On January 13, the minor planet (7) **Iris** is at opposition in **Gemini** at mag. 7.6 (see the chart on page 26).

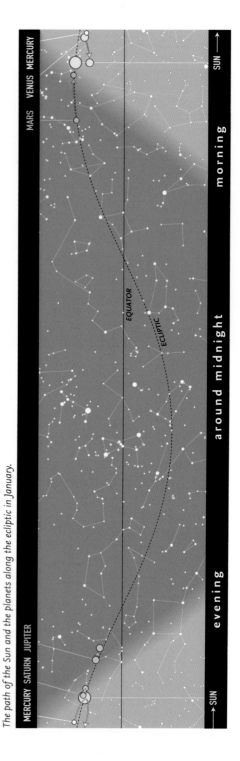

The path of the Sun and the planets along the ecliptic in January.

MERCURY SATURN JUPITER

MARS   VENUS MERCURY

evening   around midnight   morning

SUN →   → SUN

01	22:55	Moon at perigee (358,033 km)
02	18:33	New Moon
03	08:09	Venus 7.5°N of Moon
04	01:21	Mercury 3.1°N of Moon
04	06:55	Earth at perihelion (0.983337 AU = 147,105,053 km)
04	16:47	Saturn 4.2°N of Moon
06	00:11	Jupiter 4.5°N of Moon
07	09:46	Neptune 4.1°N of Moon
07	11:04	Mercury at greatest elongation (19.2°E, mag. –0.6)
09	00:48	Venus at inferior conjunction
09	18:11	First Quarter
11	11:27	Uranus 1.5°N of Moon
13	20:35	Minor planet (7) Iris at opposition (mag. 7.6)
14	01:35	Aldebaran 6°S of Moon
14	09:26	Moon at apogee = 405,805 km
17	16:13	Pollux 2.6°N of Moon
17	23:48	Full Moon
20	11:00	Regulus 4.9°S of Moon
23	10:28	Mercury at inferior conjunction
24	13:59	Spica 5.5°S of Moon
25	13:41	Last Quarter
27	23:28	Antares 3.7°S of Moon
29	15:03	Mars 2.4°N of Moon
30	01:50	Venus 10.2°N of Moon
30	07:11	Moon at perigee = 362,252 km
1–Feb 20		α-Centaurid meteor shower

Evening 9 p.m. (DST)

January 4–6 • Shortly after sunset, the narrow crescent Moon passes Mercury, Saturn and Jupiter, in the western sky.

Evening 10 p.m. (DST)

January 17 • The Moon with Castor and Pollux in the northeastern sky. Procyon is nearby.

Midnight (DST)

January 20/21 • At midnight the Moon is between Regulus and Algieba

Morning 5 a.m. (DST)

January 28–30 • The waning crescent Moon passes Antares, Sabi and Mars. Venus is closer to the horizon. The 'Cat's Eyes' and Kau

February 01   11 p.m.   (12 p.m. DST)
February 15   10 p.m.   (11 p.m. DST)

February, looking South

February – Looking South

The whole of **Centaurus** is now clear of the horizon in the southeast, where, below it, the constellation of **Lupus** is beginning to be visible. **Triangulum Australe** is now higher in the sky and easier to see. Both **Crux** and the **False Cross** are also higher and more visible. The **Large Magellanic Cloud** (LMC) and brilliant Canopus are now almost due south, with the constellation of **Puppis** at the zenith. Both **Hydrus** and the **Small Magellanic Cloud** (SMC) are lower in the sky, as is **Phoenix**, which is much closer to the horizon in the west. Next to it, the constellation of **Tucana** is also lower although the globular cluster **47 Tucanae** remains readily visible as does **Achernar** (α Eridani). The constellation of **Grus** and bright **Fomalhaut** (α Piscis Austrini) have disappeared below the horizon. **Peacock** (α Pavonis) is skimming the horizon in the south and is not easily seen at any time in the night.

Meteors

The **Centaurid** shower, which actually consists of two separate streams: the **α-** and **β-Centaurids**, with both radiants lying near α and β Centauri (Rigil Kentaurus and Hadar, respectively), continues in February, reaching a low maximum (around 5 meteors per hour) on February 8, when the Moon is a waxing crescent, just before First Quarter. Another weak shower, the **γ-Normids**, begins to be active in late February (February 25), but the meteors are difficult to differentiate from sporadics. It reaches its weak (but sharp) maximum on March 14–15.

Parts of Carina and Vela. The 'False Cross' is indicated with blue lines. The red blurry spot near the bottom-left corner is the Eta (η) Carinae Nebula. To the right, and a little lower, is an open cluster that surrounds Theta (ϑ) Carinae. This cluster (IC 2602) is also known as the Southern Pleiades.

February 01   11 p.m.   (12 p.m. DST)
February 15   10 p.m.   (11 p.m. DST)
March 01   9 p.m.   (10 p.m. DST)

February, Looking North

February – Looking North

The constellation of **Gemini**, with the pair of stars **Castor** and **Pollux** (α and β Geminorum) is now due north. Pollux is higher in the sky (farther towards the zenith), and above it is **Procyon** (α Canis Minoris), half-way to the zenith. Still higher is **Sirius**, the brightest star in the sky and the constellation of **Canis Major**. The faint constellation of **Cancer**, with its most noticeable feature, the cluster **Praesepe**, lies to the east of Gemini. Above it, and directly east of Procyon, is the distinctive asterism forming the head of **Hydra**, the whole of which constellation is now visible stretching across the sky towards the east. The constellation of **Taurus**, with orange **Aldebaran** (α Tauri) is still clearly seen in the west. By contrast, **Auriga** is much lower towards the horizon and brilliant **Capella** (α Aurigae) is extremely low and visible only early in the night. The faintest stretch of the Milky Way runs from Auriga in the northwest up towards the zenith, passing through Gemini and the indistinct constellation of **Monoceros**. In the northeast, the zodiacal constellation of **Leo** and bright **Regulus** (α Leonis) are clearly seen.

The constellation of Cancer. Almost at the centre of the image is the open star cluster M44 (Praesepe), sometimes called the 'Beehive'. The faint constellation of Cancer is surrounded by several bright stars; Castor and Pollux, near the bottom, Procyon near the top and Regulus with Algieba close to the right edge of the image (south is up).

The Moon's phases for February

New Moon							First Quarter								Full Moon
01 05:46	**02**	**03**	**04**	**05**	**06**	**07**	**08** 13:50	**09**	**10**	**11**	**12**	**13**	**14**	**15**	**16** 16:56
Day 1	Day 2	Day 3	Day 4	Day 5	Day 6	Day 7	Day 8	Day 9	Day 10	Day 11	Day 12	Day 13	Day 14	Day 15	Day 16

					Last Quarter							
17	**18**	**19**	**20**	**21**	**22**	**23** 22:32	**24**	**25**	**26**	**27**	**28**	
Day 17	Day 18	Day 19	Day 20	Day 21	Day 22	Day 23	Day 24	Day 25	Day 26	Day 27	Day 28	

February – Moon and Planets

The Moon

Just after New Moon on February 1, the Moon passes 4.2° south of **Saturn**. The next day it is a similar distance south of **Jupiter**, low on the western horizon. On February 7 the Moon is 1.2° south of **Uranus** in **Aries**. On February 10, waxing gibbous, it is 6.7° north of **Aldebaran** in **Taurus**. On February 13 it is 2.6° south of **Pollux** in **Gemini** and just after Full Moon on February 16 it is 4.8° north of **Regulus** in **Leo**. The waning gibbous Moon is 5.3° north of **Spica** on February 20, and, one day past Last Quarter, 3.4° north of **Antares** on February 24. On February 27, a waning crescent, it is south of **Venus** and **Mars**, and these are low in the morning twilight.

Occultations

In 2022 there are no lunar occultations of the five brightest stars near the ecliptic: **Aldebaran, Antares, Pollux, Regulus** and **Spica**. There are two occultations of **Venus**, one on May 27, visible over a restricted area of the Indian Ocean only, and one on October 25, invisible in daylight. There are three occultations of **Mars**, only one visible, with difficulty, from Western Europe and North America on December 8 at Full Moon. There are no occultations of **Jupiter** or **Saturn**.

The planets

Mercury is at greatest elongation 26.3° west in the morning sky on February 16. **Venus** is in **Sagittarius**, visible in the morning sky and 7° north of **Mars** on February 13. Mars is also in Sagittarius, but becomes very low towards the end of the month and difficult to see. **Jupiter** and **Saturn** are too close to the Sun to be visible. Saturn is at superior conjunction on February 4. **Uranus** remains in **Aries** at mag. 5.8, and **Neptune** in **Aquarius** at mag. 7.9 to 8.0.

The path of the Sun and the planets along the ecliptic in February.

Calendar for February

01	05:46	New Moon
01	08:57	Saturn 4.2°N of Moon
02	21:10	Jupiter 4.3°N of Moon
03	21:13	Neptune 3.9°N of Moon
04	19:05	Saturn at superior conjunction
07	19:39	Uranus 1.2°N of Moon
08		α-Centaurid meteor shower maximum
08	13:50	First Quarter
10	08:53	Aldebaran 6.7°S of Moon
11	02:37	Moon at apogee = 404,897 km
13	01:00 *	Mars 7.0°S of Venus
13	23:28	Pollux 2.6°N of Moon
16	16:56	Full Moon
16	17:46	Regulus 4.8°S of Moon
16	21:07	Mercury at greatest elongation (26.3°W, mag. -0.0)
20	19:34	Spica 5.3°S of Moon
23	22:32	Last Quarter
24	05:50	Antares 3.4°S of Moon
25–Mar.28		γ-Normid meteor shower
26	22:25	Moon at perigee = 367,789 km
27	06:28	Venus 8.7°N of Moon
27	08:59	Mars 3.5°N of Moon
28	20:05	Mercury 3.7°N of Moon
28	23:45	Saturn 4.3°N of Moon

* These objects are close together for an extended period around this time.

Evening 8:30 p.m. (DST)

Fomalhaut · Jupiter · 2 · 3 · WSW · W · 10°

February 2–3 • After sunset, the narrow crescent Moon passes Jupiter. Fomalhaut is a little higher in the Westsouthwest.

Morning 6 a.m. (DST)

Kaus Australis · Nunki · Mars · Mercury · Venus · ESE · E · 10° · 30°

February 13 • Mercury, Venus and Mars are in the eastern sky, together with Nunki and Kaus Australis.

Evening 11 p.m. (DST)

Regulus · Algieba · 16 · 17 · 18 · Denebola · E · 10° · -25°

February 16–18 • The Full Moon passes Regulus and Algieba. On February 18 it is close to Denebola.

Morning 4 a.m. (DST)

Acrab · Dschubba · 24 · Antares · 25 · Sabik · E · 10° · -45°

February 24–25 • The Moon passes Acrab (β Sco), Dschubba (δ Sco) and Antares.

Morning 5 a.m. (DST)

Nunki · 27 · Mars · Venus · 28 · E · ESE · 10°

February 27–28 • The Moon with Nunki, Mars and Venus in the morning sky.

N

ORION
Betelgeuse
M42 Orion Nebula
Rigel
LEPUS

MONOCEROS

Sirius
CANIS
MAJOR
Adhara

COLUMBA

ERIDANUS

FORNAX

CAELUM

DORADO

HOROLOGIUM

RETICULUM

PHOENIX

Achernar

Canopus

PICTOR

PUPPIS

CARINA

LMC

SMC

47 Tucanae

TUCANA

PYXIS

False Cross

Tarantula
Nebula

MENSA

HYDRUS

VELA

VOLANS

CHAMAELEON

OCTANS

INDUS

S

Ghost of Jupiter

ZENITH

ANTLIA

Eta Carinae
Nebula

Southern
Pleiades

MUSCA

APUS

PAVO

Peacock

Acrux
CRUX
Mimosa
Jewel Box
Coalsack
Hadar
Rigil Kentaurus

TRIANGULUM
AUSTRALE

TELESCOPIUM

CRATER

HYDRA

CENTAURUS

Omega
Centauri

CIRCINUS

ARA

CORVUS

Menkent

LUPUS

NORMA

γ-Normids

Cat's Eyes

Spica

ECLIPTIC

VIRGO

LIBRA

SCORPIUS

M4
Antares

BOÖTES

E

The constellation of Vela may be found in the lower part of the image, as well as the False Cross, consisting of two stars that belong to Vela, while the two stars near the bottom are part of Carina. The constellation of Pyxis is near the top (north is up).

March – Looking South

The Sun crosses the celestial equator on Sunday, March 20, at the equinox, when day and night are of almost equal length, and the southern season of autumn is considered to begin. (The hours of daylight and darkness change most rapidly around the equinoxes in March and September.)

Scorpius is beginning to become visible in the eastern sky, including the 'Cat's Eyes', the pair of stars **Shaula** and **Lesath** (λ and υ Scorpii, respectively) at the end of the 'sting'. Above Scorpius, the whole of the constellation of **Lupus** is now easy to see. The magnificent globular cluster of **Omega Centauri** is now readily visible, north-east of **Crux**. The **Coalsack** and the denser region of the Milky Way in **Carina**, together with the **Eta Carinae Nebula** and the **Southern Pleiades** are well placed for observation. The **False Cross** on the **Carina/Vela** border is now high in the sky, between the South Celestial Pole and the zenith. Brilliant **Canopus** (α Carinae) is only slightly lower towards the west, above the **Large Magellanic Cloud** (LMC) and the striking **Tarantula Nebula**. **Achernar** (α Eridani), the **Small Magellanic Cloud** (SMC) and **47 Tucanae** are considerably lower, but still clear of the horizon. **Peacock** (α Pavonis) remains low, skimming the horizon, just east of south. **Orion** is now visibly getting lower in the west, and is being followed by **Sirius** and **Canis Major**.

Meteors

The only significant meteor shower in March is the **γ-Normids**, which have a low rate, and are thus difficult to differentiate from sporadics. However, they exhibit a very sharp peak a day or so on either side of maximum on March 14–15, when the Moon is waxing gibbous, which will cause considerable interference. The faint constellation of **Norma** rises early in the night, but most meteors are likely to be seen (away from the radiant) in the hours after midnight.

March – Looking North

Almost due north is the constellation of **Leo**, with the 'backward question mark' (or 'Sickle') of bright stars forming the head of the mythological lion. **Regulus** (α Leonis) – the 'dot' of the 'question mark' or the handle of the sickle and the brightest star in Leo – lies very close to the ecliptic and is one of the few first-magnitude stars that may be occulted by the Moon, although none occur in 2022. The Moon often passes between Regulus and **Algieba** (γ Leonis). To the west lies the faint constellation of **Cancer**, with the open cluster M44, or **Praesepe**. The constellations of **Gemini** and **Orion** are now getting low in the west, but above them, both **Procyon** in **Canis Minor** and the constellation of **Canis Major** remain clear to see. The whole of **Hydra** (the largest constellation) now sprawls right across the southern and eastern skies, and the three small constellations of **Sextans**, **Crater** and **Corvus** are readily visible. The unremarkable constellation of **Antlia** is at the zenith. In the east, **Arcturus** (α Boötis) – the brightest star in the northern hemisphere of the sky – is becoming visible, and climbs higher during the night.

The distinctive constellation of Leo, with Regulus and 'The Sickle' on the west. Algieba (γ Leonis), north of Regulus, appearing double, is a multiple system of four stars (south is up).

The Moon's phases for March

New Moon

| 01 | 02 17:35 | 03 | 04 | 05 | 06 | 07 | 08 | 09 | 10 10:45 | 11 | 12 | 13 | 14 | 15 | 16 |
| Day 29 | Day 30 | Day 1 | Day 2 | Day 3 | Day 4 | Day 5 | Day 6 | Day 7 | Day 8 | Day 9 | Day 10 | Day 11 | Day 12 | Day 13 | Day 14 |

First Quarter

Full Moon

| 17 | 18 07:18 | 19 | 20 | 21 | 22 | 23 | 24 | 25 05:37 | 26 | 27 | 28 | 29 | 30 | 31 | |
| Day 15 | Day 16 | Day 17 | Day 18 | Day 19 | Day 20 | Day 21 | Day 22 | Day 23 | Day 24 | Day 25 | Day 26 | Day 27 | Day 28 | Day 29 | |

Last Quarter

March – Moon and Planets

The Moon

On March 7, the waxing crescent Moon is 0.8° south of *Uranus* (mag. 5.8) in *Aries*. On March 9, just before First Quarter, it is 7.0° north of *Aldebaran*. On March 13, the waxing gibbous Moon passes 2.4° south of *Pollux* in *Gemini*. On March 16, two days before Full, the Moon is 4.9° north of *Regulus*. On March 20, two days after Full Moon, it is 5.1° north of *Spica* in *Virgo*. On March 23 it is 3.2° north of *Antares* in *Scorpius* and on March 28 the waning crescent Moon passes south of both *Mars* and *Venus*.

The Planets

Mercury is too close to the Sun to be seen. *Venus*, visible in the morning sky, is very bright (mag. -4.7 to -4.5) and is at western elongation on March 20. *Mars* is also in the morning sky, initially in *Sagittarius*, but moving into *Capricornus* and fading slightly to mag. 1.1. *Jupiter* is at superior conjunction in *Aquarius* on March 5, but is too close to the Sun to be visible this month. *Saturn* is in *Capricornus*, and very low in the morning sky. *Uranus* is in *Aries* at mag. 5.8. *Neptune* (mag. 8.0) is at superior conjunction on March 13.

The path of the Sun and the planets along the ecliptic in March.

Calendar for March

02	13:00 *	Mercury 0.7°S of Saturn
02	17:35	New Moon
02	18:35	Jupiter 4.1°N of Moon
03	09:02	Neptune 3.7°N of Moon
05	14:07	Jupiter at superior conjunction
07	06:08	Uranus 0.8°N of Moon
09	16:59	Aldebaran 7.0°S of Moon
10	10:45	First Quarter
10	23:04	Moon at apogee = 404,268 km
12	14:00 *	Mars 4.0°S of Venus
13	07:34	Pollux 2.4°N of Moon
13	11:43	Neptune at superior conjunction
14–15		γ-Normid meteor shower maximum
16	02:00	Regulus 4.9°S of Moon
18	07:18	Full Moon
20	02:24	Spica 5.1°S of Moon
20	09:25	Venus at greatest elongation (46.6°W, mag. −4.5)
20	15:33	Autumnal (southern) equinox
23	11:16	Antares 3.2°S of Moon
23	23:37	Moon at perigee = 369,760 km
25	05:37	Last Quarter
28	02:53	Mars 4.1°N of Moon
28	09:49	Venus 6.7°N of Moon
28	11:41	Saturn 4.4°N of Moon
29	13:00 *	Saturn 2.2°S of Venus
30	14:36	Jupiter 3.9°N of Moon
30	19:18	Neptune 3.7°N of Moon

These objects are close together for an extended period around this time.

Morning 6:15 a.m. (DST)

March 1–2 • *Shortly before sunrise, the narrow crescent Moon passes Mercury and Saturn. Fomalhaut is farther southeast.*

Evening 8 p.m. (DST)

March 13 • *The Moon aligns with the twin stars, Castor and Pollux. At magnitude 1.6, Castor is slightly fainter than Pollux (magnitude 1.2).*

Morning 5 a.m. (DST)

March 28–29 • *In the east, the waning crescent Moon passes Mars, Venus and Saturn.*

After midnight 1 a.m. (DST)

March 24 • *The Moon is in the company of Antares, Acrab (β Sco) and Dschubba (δ Sco).*

Evening 11 p.m. (DST)

March 15–16 • *The Moon passes between Regulus and Algieba.*

April | Looking South

April 01   11 p.m.   (12 p.m. DST)
April 15   10 p.m.
May 01   9 p.m.

April – Looking South

Daylight Saving Time ends in both Australia and New Zealand on Sunday, April 3 with the arrival of autumn. **Crux** is now high in the south, with the two brightest stars of **Centaurus** (α and β Centauri, *Rigil Kentaurus* and *Hadar*, respectively) to its east. The magnificent globular cluster, *Omega Centauri*, is readily visible high in the sky. West of Crux, both the **Southern Pleiades** and the *Eta Carinae Nebula* are clearly seen, two-thirds of the way towards the zenith. Farther west, the *False Cross* is beginning to decline towards the horizon. *Canopus* (α Carinae) is even lower, and **Orion** has now disappeared below the horizon. **Canis Major** and brilliant *Sirius* are also descending in the west. *Achernar* (α Eridani) is skimming the southern horizon, but *Peacock* (α Pavonis) is now slightly higher and more easily visible. Although the **LMC** is roughly as high as the South Celestial Pole, the **SMC** and *47 Tucanae* are rather low (but still visible) in the south. In the east, the whole of **Scorpius** is now well clear of the horizon with the inconspicuous constellation of **Libra** preceding it along the ecliptic. The dense regions of the Milky Way in **Sagittarius** become visible later in the night.

Meteors

Two meteor showers, in particular, occur in April. The *π-Puppid* shower begins on April 15, but conditions are not particularly favourable in 2022 with shower maximum on April 23–24, when the Moon is 23–24 days old (at and just after Last Quarter). The hourly rate is variable but the meteors tend to be faint. The parent body is the comet 26P/Grigg-Skjellerup. A second, more prolific, shower, the *η-Aquarids*, begins on April 19, just after Full Moon, and continues into May.

Omega Centauri (NGC 5139) is the largest and finest globular cluster in the sky (and in the Milky Way galaxy). It is believed to contain 10 million stars and differs in chemical composition and nature so greatly from other globulars that it may be the core of a disrupted dwarf galaxy, captured by the far more massive Galaxy.

April   Looking North

April 01   11 p.m.   (12 p.m. DST)
April 15   10 p.m.
May 01   9 p.m.

April – Looking North

Leo is the most prominent constellation in the northern sky in April. *Gemini*, with *Castor* and *Pollux*, is low on the horizon in the west, and *Cancer* lies between the two constellations. To the east of Leo, the whole of *Virgo*, with *Spica* (α Virginis) its brightest star, is clearly visible, with the constellation of *Libra* farther east along the ecliptic. Above Leo and Virgo, the complete length of *Hydra* is visible, with *Alphard* (α Hydrae) forming a prominent triangle with *Regulus* and *Procyon* in *Canis Minor*. High in the sky, the small constellations of *Sextans* and *Crater*, together with the rather brighter *Corvus* lie between Leo, Virgo and Hydra.

Boötes and *Arcturus* are prominent in the northeastern sky, together with the globular cluster M3 in *Canes Venatici*. The circlet of *Corona Borealis* is close to the horizon. Between Leo and Boötes lies the constellation of *Coma Berenices*, notable for being the location of the open cluster Melotte 111 (this is sometimes called the Coma Cluster and confused with the Coma Cluster of galaxies (Abell 1656) east of *Denebola* in *Leo*). There are about 1,000 galaxies in Abell 1656, shown on the chart on page 61, and which is located near the North Galactic Pole, where we are looking out of the plane of the Galaxy and are thus

A very large, and frequently ignored, open star cluster, Melotte 111, also known as the Coma Cluster, is readily visible in the northern sky during April and May (south is up).

able to see deep into space. Only about ten of the brightest galaxies in the Coma Cluster are visible with the largest amateur telescopes.

The Moon's phases for April

April – Moon and Planets

The Moon

On April 3, the narrow waxing crescent Moon (two days old) passes 0.6° south of *Uranus* (mag. 5.8) in *Aries* in the evening sky. On April 6, still a waxing crescent, it passes 7.2° north of orange *Aldebaran* in *Taurus*. At First Quarter on April 9, it is 2.2° south of *Pollux* in *Gemini*. It passes 5.1° north of *Regulus* on April 12 and the same distance north of *Spica* in *Virgo* on April 16. (Both events occur in daylight.) On April 19, the Moon is 3.1° north of *Antares* and on April 24, 4.5° south of *Saturn* in *Capricornus*. Two days after Last Quarter, on April 25, the Moon is 3.9° south of *Mars*. On April 27, it passes, in succession, south of *Venus*, *Neptune* and *Jupiter*, very low in the morning sky. On April 30, there is a partial solar eclipse, visible only from Chile and Argentina just before sunset.

The planets

Most of the planets are low in the sky this month. *Mercury* is largely invisible. It is at superior conjunction on April 2, but comes to greatest eastern elongation (20.6° from the Sun at mag. 0.2) on April 29. *Venus* is bright (mag. -4.5 to -4.1) but very low in the morning sky. *Mars* (mag. 1.1 to 0.9) moves from *Capricornus* into *Aquarius*, but is also low in the morning sky. On April 4, it is 0.3° south of *Saturn* and both are of similar magnitude (mag. 1.1 and 0.9). *Jupiter*, again very low in the morning sky (fading slightly from mag. -2.1), is initially just within *Aquarius*, and then moves into *Pisces*. *Saturn* (mag. 0.9) is in *Capricornus*. *Uranus* (mag. 5.9) is slowly moving eastwards in *Aries*. *Neptune*, in *Pisces*, is mag. 8.0 to 7.9.

The path of the Sun and the planets along the ecliptic in April.

01	00:25	Mercury 2.6°N of Moon
01	06:24	New Moon
02	23:11	Mercury at superior conjunction
02		Australian and New Zealand Daylight Saving Time ends
03	17:27	Uranus 0.6°N of Moon
04	22:00 *	Mars 0.3°S of Saturn
06	01:16	Aldebaran 7.2°S of Moon
07	19:11	Moon at apogee = 404,438 km
09	06:48	First Quarter
09	15:50	Pollux 2.2°N of Moon
2	20:00 *	Neptune 0.1°S of Jupiter
2	11:01	Regulus 5.1°S of Moon
5–28		π-Puppid meteor shower
6	11:19	Spica 5.1°S of Moon
6	18:55	Full Moon
8	14:00 *	Uranus 2.1°S of Mercury
9–May.28		η-Aquariid meteor shower
9	15:13	Moon at perigee = 365,143 km
9	18:08	Antares 3.1°S of Moon
3	11:56	Last Quarter
3–24		π-Puppid meteor shower maximum
4	20:55	Saturn 4.5°N of Moon
5	22:05	Mars 3.9°N of Moon
7	01:51	Venus 3.8°N of Moon
7	03:20	Neptune 3.7°N of Moon
7	08:26	Jupiter 3.7°N of Moon
27	19:00 *	Neptune 0.01°N of Venus
9	08:09	Mercury at greatest elongation (20.6°E, mag. 0.2)
0	19:00 *	Venus 0.3°S of Jupiter
0	20:28	New Moon
0	20:41	Partial solar eclipse

These objects are close togeth... for an extend...

Morning 5:30 a.m.

April 5 • Saturn and Mars are close together, with Venus below them. Jupiter is closer to the horizon.

Evening 8 p.m.

April 9 • The First Quarter Moon with Castor and Pollux. Alhena is farther northwest.

Early morning 4 a.m.

April 20 • The Moon is close to Antares, at a height of 70°. Acrab, Dschubba and Sabik are nearby.

Early morning 4 a.m.

April 25 • The Moon with Saturn high in the east. Moon is directly below them and Fomalhaut is farther

Morning 5 a.m.

April 26–28 • The Moon is a waning crescent when it passes three planets in the eastern sky. Mars, Venus

May — Looking South

May 01   11 p.m.
May 15   10 p.m.
June 01   9 p.m.

+ SCP

May – Looking South

In the west, **Canis Major** has set below the horizon, and **Canopus** (α Carinae) and **Puppis** are getting rather low. The whole of **Sagittarius** is now clearly seen in the east, with **Corona Australis** beneath it and **Scorpius** higher above. **Centaurus** is fully seen high in the south, with **Crux**, the **Eta Carinae Nebula**, the **Southern Pleiades** and the **False Cross** with **Vela** along the Milky Way to the west. In the south, **Achernar** (α Eridani) is skimming the southern horizon and the **Small Magellanic Cloud** (SMC) is beginning to rise higher in the sky, unlike the **Large Magellanic Cloud** (LMC) which is now lower. **Pavo** and **Peacock** (α Pavonis) are now much higher and even the faint constellations of **Tucana** and **Indus** are visible between Pavo and the southwestern horizon.

Meteors

The **η-Aquariids** are one of the two meteor showers associated with Comet 1P/Halley (the other being the **Orionids**, in October). The radiant is near the celestial equator, close to the 'Water Jar' in **Aquarius**, well below the horizon until late in the night (around dawn). However, meteors may still be seen in the eastern sky even when the radiant is below the horizon. There is a radiant map for the η-Aquariids on page 30. Their maximum in 2022, on May 6, occurs when the Moon is a waxing crescent, so conditions are reasonably favourable. Maximum hourly rate is about 50 per hour and a large proportion (about 25 per cent) of the meteors leave persistent trains.

Some faint constellations around the South Celestial Pole (SCP). Below the Pole, a part of the constellation of Octans is visible. Then, a little lower, Apus and farther down, Triangulum Australe. To the left is Musca and just above the centre of the image is Chamaeleon. The bright star near the top edge of the image is Miaplacidus, in the constellation of Carina.

MIC

SAGITTARIUS

Nunki

Kaus Australis

Teapot

M22

CORONA AUSTRALIS

TELESCOPIUM

SCUTUM

M11
Wild Duck Cluster

SERPENS CAUDA

M8 Lagoon Nebula

M7

Cat's Eyes

AQUILA

E

ARA

SCORPIUS

NORMA

Antares

M4

LUPUS

Sabik

OPHIUCHUS

LIBRA

HERCULES

Keystone

SERPENS CAPUT

Menkent

CENTAURUS

ZENITH

HYDRA

Omega Centauri

Alphecca

CORONA BOREALIS

M13

CORVUS

Arcturus

Spica

VIRGO

M3

BOÖTES

CRATER

Virgo Cluster
See finder chart
on page 61

CANES VENATICI

URSA MAJOR

N

Denebola

COMA BERENICES

Melotte 111

LEO MINOR

ECLIPTIC

CRATER

Ghost of Jupiter

SEXTANS

Regulus

LEO

ANTLIA

Algieba

VELA

Alphard

HYDRA

CANCER

M67

PUPPIS

MONOCEROS

COLUMBA

Adhara

CANIS MAJOR

W

May 01   11 p.m.
May 15   10 p.m.

May – Looking North

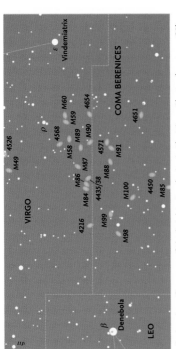

Boötes is almost due north, with brilliant, slightly orange-coloured **Arcturus** extemely prominent. The distinctive circlet of **Corona Borealis** is clearly visible to its east. The brightest star (α Coronae Borealis) is known as **Alphecca**. **Hercules** is rising in the east and becomes clearly visible later in the night. To the west of Boötes is the inconspicuous constellation of **Coma Berenices**, with the cluster **Melote 111** (see page 55) and, above it, the Virgo Cluster of galaxies (see here).

The large constellation of **Ophiuchus** (which actually crosses the ecliptic, and is thus the 'thirteenth' zodiacal constellation) is climbing into the eastern sky. Before the constellation boundaries were formally adopted by the International Astronomical Union in 1930, the southern region of Ophiuchus was regarded as forming part of the constellation of Scorpius, which had been part of the zodiac since antiquity.

Early in the night, the constellation of **Virgo**, with **Spica** (α Virginis), lies due north, with the rather faint constellation of **Libra** to its east. Farther along the ecliptic are **Scorpius** and brilliant, reddish **Antares** (α Scorpii). In the west, the constellation of **Leo** is readily visible now, and

both **Regulus** and **Denebola** (α and β Leonis, respectively) are prominent.

Virgo contains the nearest large cluster of galaxies, which is the centre of the Local Supercluster, of which the Milky Way galaxy forms part. The Virgo Cluster contains some 2,000 galaxies, the brightest of which are visible in amateur telescopes.

A finder chart for some of the brightest galaxies in the Virgo Cluster (see page 60). All stars brighter than magnitude 8.5 are shown (south is up).

The Moon's phases for May

May – Moon and Planets

The Moon

On May 1, one day after New Moon, a very thin crescent Moon passes 0.4° south of *Uranus* (mag. 5.9) in Pisces, 0.4° south of *Uranus* (mag. 5.9) in *Aries*, very low in the morning sky. The Moon is 2.1° south of *Pollux* on May 6. It is 5.1° north of *Regulus* in *Leo* on May 9. On May 13, waxing gibbous, it is 5.1° north of *Spica* in *Virgo*. On May 16 there is a total lunar eclipse (see page 20). The next day, the Moon is 3.1° north of *Antares*. On May 22, at Last Quarter, it is 4.5° south of *Saturn*. Two days later it passes 2.8° south of *Mars* and then 3.3° south of *Jupiter* in *Pisces*. By May 28, a narrow waning crescent, it is just 0.3° south of *Uranus* in *Aries*.

The planets

Mercury is lost in daylight throughout May. *Venus* (mag. -4.0), in Pisces, moves closer to the Sun, becoming lost in morning twilight. There is an occultation of the planet on May 27, but this is essentially invisible, occurring in daylight and only visible from a small area of the southern Indian Ocean. *Mars* (mag. 0.9 to 0.7) moves from *Aquarius* into *Pisces*, in the morning sky. *Jupiter* (mag. -2.1 to -2.2) is also just inside Pisces. *Saturn* (mag. 0.8) is in *Capricornus*. *Uranus* is in *Aries* at mag. 5.9 and comes to superior conjunction on May 5. *Neptune* remains in *Pisces* at mag. 7.9.

The path of the Sun and the planets along the ecliptic in May.

Calendar for May

01	04:10	Uranus 0.4°N of Moon
02	14:18	Mercury 1.9°N of Moon
03	08:57	Aldebaran 7.2°S of Moon
05	07:21	Uranus at superior conjunction
05	12:46	Moon at apogee = 405,285 km
06		η-Aquariid meteor shower maximum
06	23:32	Pollux 2.1°N of Moon
09	00:21	First Quarter
09	19:40	Regulus 5.1°S of Moon
13	21:29	Spica 5.1°S of Moon
16	04:11	Total lunar eclipse
16	04:14	Full Moon
17	03:19	Antares 3.1°S of Moon
17	15:27	Moon at perigee = 360,298 km
17	23:00 *	Neptune 0.6°N of Mars
21	19:18	Mercury at inferior conjunction
22	04:43	Saturn 4.5°N of Moon
22	18:43	Last Quarter
24	10:01	Neptune 3.7°N of Moon
24	19:23	Mars 2.8°N of Moon
25	00:02	Jupiter 3.3°N of Moon
27	02:51	Venus 0.2°N of Moon
28	13:42	Uranus 0.3°N of Moon
29	00:00 *	Mars 0.6°S of Jupiter
29	12:53	Mercury 3.7°S of Moon
30	11:30	New Moon
30	15:38	Aldebaran 7.2°S of Moon

*These objects are close together for an extended period around this time.

Morning 5 a.m.

May 1 • Venus and Jupiter are separated by only 0.3°. Mars is about 15° above the couple.

Evening 5:30 p.m.

May 2–3 • The crescent Moon passes Aldebaran, Mercury and the Pleiades, which will probably be lost in twilight.

Evening 8 p.m.

May 9–11 • Just after First Quarter the Moon passes Regulus, Algieba and Denebola.

Morning 6 a.m.

May 25–27 • Shortly before sunrise, the waning crescent Moon passes Mars, Jupiter and Venus.

Evening 8 p.m.

May 16–18 • The Moon passes Dschubba, Acrab, Antares and Sabik. The 'Cat's Eyes' and Kaus Australis are nearby.

June – Looking South

Both **Canopus** (α Carinae) and **Achernar** (α Eridani) are skimming the southern horizon. Although the whole of **Carina** is visible, all of **Eridanus** (except **Achernar**) is hidden below the horizon. The **Large Magellanic Cloud** (LMC) is low, altough the **Small Magellanic Cloud** (SMC), the globular cluster, **47 Tucanae** and **Hydrus** are now rather higher. **Alphard** (α Hydrae) is on the horizon, and the constellation of **Sextans** is becoming low. However, the remainder of the long constellation of Hydra is clearly seen as are the two constellations of **Crater** and **Corvus** to its north. The **False Cross** between Carina and **Vela** is beginning to descend in the west, but Vela itself is clearly visible. The whole of both **Crux** and **Centaurus** are clearly seen, as are the magnificent globular cluster, **Omega Centauri**, and the constellation of **Lupus**, closer to the zenith. The constellation of **Triangulum Australe** is on the meridian, roughly half-way between the South Celestial Pole and the zenith. Both **Scorpius**, with brilliant, red **Antares** (α Scorpii) and **Sagittarius** are high overhead, with the faint constellation of **Corona Australis** visible below them. The whole of **Capricornus** is visible, and the constellation of **Grus** has now risen above the horizon, with the faint constellation of **Indus** between it and **Pavo**. To the east of Grus is **Piscis Austrinus**, although brilliant **Fomalhaut** (α Piscis Austrini) is only just clear of the horizon, and becomes clearly visible only later in the night and later in the month.

The distinctive shape of the zodiacal constellation of Scorpius. The red supergiant star, Antares is close to the zenith in June. The bright spot near the left side of the image is the open cluster M7, also known as Ptolomy's Cluster (north is up).

June – Looking North

June 01		11 p.m.
June 15		10 p.m.
July 01		9 p.m.

June – Looking North

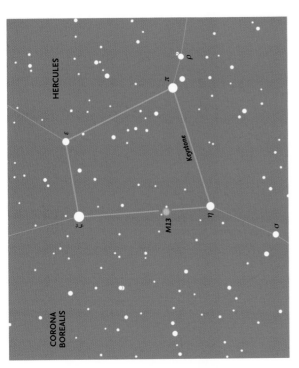

Vega in **Lyra** is just above the northeastern horizon. Closer to the meridian, the whole of **Hercules** is visible including the **'Keystone'** and **M13**, widely regarded as the finest globular cluster in the northern hemisphere. The small constellation of **Corona Borealis** is almost due north. To the west of the meridian is **Boötes** and **Arcturus** (α Boötis). Much of **Leo** is now below the western horizon, but **Denebola** (β Leonis) is still visible. Higher in the sky, the whole of **Virgo** is clearly visible and, still higher, not far from the zenith is the constellation of **Libra**. To its east is **Scorpius** and reddish **Antares**. Farther along the ecliptic, both the constellations of **Sagittarius** and **Capricornus** are completely visible. Between Hercules and Sagittarius is the large constellation of **Ophiuchus** and, to its east, **Aquila** and **Altair** (α Aquilae), one of the stars of the (northern) Summer Triangle. Another of the three stars, **Vega** in **Lyra**, is skimming the northern horizon.

Finder chart for M13, the finest globular cluster in the northern sky. All stars down to magnitude 7.5 are shown (south is up).

The Moon's phases for June

June – Moon and Planets

The Moon

On June 3, the waxing crescent Moon will be 2.1° south of **Pollux** in **Gemini**. One day before First Quarter, on June 6, it will be 5.1° north of **Regulus**. On June 10, it will be 5.0° north of **Spica** in **Virgo**. On June 13, nearly Full, and in daylight, it passes 3.1° north of **Antares**. After Full Moon on June 18, it is at the closest perigee of the year. On June 18, in daylight, it passes **Saturn** and on June 21, it is 2.7° south of **Jupiter** (again in daylight). It is 0.9° south of **Mars** the following day (June 22). As in May, it passes just south (0.1°) of Uranus on June 24. On June 26, in morning twilight, it passes 2.7° north of **Venus**. Later that day, it is 7.2° north of **Aldebaran** in **Taurus**, low in the twilight. On June 30, just after New Moon, it is 2.2° south of **Pollux**.

The planets

Mercury is at greatest western elongation (23.2°) on June 16, but too low to be readily visible. **Venus** (mag. -3.9), initially on the borders of **Pisces** and **Aries**, swiftly closes with the Sun and becomes low in the evening sky. **Mars** (mag. 0.7 to 0.5) is moving eastwards in Pisces. **Jupiter** (mag. -2.3 to -2.4) is in **Pisces**. **Saturn** (mag. 0.7 to 0.6) is still within **Capricornus**, but begins retrograde motion on June 6. **Uranus** is slowly moving eastwards in **Aries**, brightening very slightly from mag. 5.9 to mag. 5.8. **Neptune** remains in **Pisces** at mag. 7.9.

The path of the Sun and the planets along the ecliptic in June.

Evening 6 p.m.

Procyon
Alhena
Pollux
Castor

↤ 10° ↦

WNW

une 3 • The crescent Moon is close to Pollux, with
Castor directly below them. Alhena and Procyon are
farther west.

Midnight

↤ 10° ↦

Cat's Eyes
ZENITH +
Antares
Dschubba
Acrab
Sabik

NW ↗

June 13/14 • The Moon with Antares, in the company
of Acrab (β Sco), Dschubba (δ Sco) and Sabik. The
'Cat's Eyes' are close to the zenith.

Early morning 3 a.m.

↤ 10° ↦

Jupiter
22
23
Mars
24

ENE
E

une 22–24 • In the early morning, the Moon passes
Jupiter and Mars in the east-northeast.

Morning 6:30 a.m.

↤ 10° ↦

Pleiades
26
Venus
27
Aldebaran
Mercury
Bellatrix

NE
ENE

June 26–27 • The crescent Moon passes the Pleiades,
Venus, Aldebaran and Mercury. Bellatrix (γ Ori) is

July – Looking South

Part of the central Milky Way in the constellations of Norma and Scorpius, showing the dark clouds of obscuring dust (north is up).

Although the **Large Magellanic Cloud** (LMC) is almost due south, it is very low. Slightly farther west, the **False Cross** is nearing the horizon. Some of **Hydra** remains visible, but the constellation of **Crater** is becoming very low. **Corvus** is still easy to see. The zodiacal constellation of **Virgo** will soon be disappearing in the west. **Crux**, **Centaurus** and **Lupus** are still clearly seen, high in the sky, as is **Scorpius**, the tail of which is near the zenith. **Achernar** (α Eridani), **Hydrus** and the **Small Magellanic Cloud** (SMC) are now higher above the horizon and easier to observe. The whole of the constellation of **Phoenix** is also now clear of the horizon. Above it are **Tucana** and, halfway to the zenith, the constellation of **Pavo**. **Grus** and **Pisces Austrinus** (with brilliant **Fomalhaut**) are now fully visible. Higher in the sky are the zodiacal constellations of **Capricornus** and **Aquarius**, and even the westernmost portion of **Pisces** is rising above the horizon.

Meteors

July brings increasing meteor activity, mainly because there are several minor radiants active in the constellations of **Capricornus** and **Aquarius**. The first shower, the **α-Capricornids**, active from July 3 to August 15 (peaking July 30), does often produce very bright fireballs. The maximum rate, however, is only about 5 per hour. The parent body is Comet 169P/NEAT. The most prominent shower is probably that of the **δ-Aquariids**, which are active from around July 12 to August 23, also with a peak on July 30, although even then the hourly rate is unlikely to reach 20 meteors per hour. In this case, the parent body is possibly Comet 96P/Machholz. This year, both shower maxima occur when the Moon is a crescent, just after New Moon, so conditions are favourable. The **Piscis Austrinids** begin on July 15 and continue until August 10. Maximum is on July 28, but the rate is only about 5 per hour. The **Perseids** begin on July 28 and peak on August 12–13.

SCULPTOR

SCULPTOR

Fomalhaut

GRUS

Piscis
Austrinis

PISCIS AUSTRINUS

PISCES

INDUS

AQUARIUS

Water Jar

PEGASUS

Southern δ-Aquariids

MICROSCOPIUM

CAPRICORNUS

SATURN

EQUULEUS

M15

DELPHINUS

α-Capricornids

AQUILA

Altair

SAGITTA

M27
Dumbbell Nebula

TELESCOPIUM

SAGITTARIUS

Nunki

Teapot

M22

SCUTUM

M11
Wild Duck Cluster

Great   Rift

SERPENS
CAUDA

VULPECULA

CYGNUS

Deneb

CORONA
AUSTRALIS

Kaus Australis

ARA

M7

Cat's
Eyes

ZENITH

M8 Lagoon
Nebula

M20
Trifid Nebula

OPHIUCHUS

M57
Ring Nebula

LYRA

Vega

N

DRACO

NORMA

Antares

SCORPIUS

M4

Sabik

HERCULES

Keystone

LUPUS

M13

LIBRA

SERPENS
CAPUT

CENTAURUS

Menkent

Omega Centauri

ECLIPTIC

CORONA BOREALIS

Alphecca

COMA
BERENICES

M3

BOÖTES

Arcturus

CORVUS

Spica

VIRGO

ANTLIA

HYDRA

CRATER

E

W

July 01   11 p.m.
July 15   10 p.m.

July, Looking North

July – Looking North

The constellations of **Hercules** and **Lyra** are on either side of the meridian and both are clearly visible well above the horizon. To the east, **Deneb** (α Cygni) is skimming the horizon, but nearly all of the rest of the constellation is easily seen as is **Aquila** with **Altair** (α Aquilae). Between **Cygnus** and Aquila lies the small constellation of **Sagitta**, with **M27** (the Dumbbell Nebula, a planetary nebula). Even farther east, the whole extent of both the zodiacal constellations of **Aquarius** and **Capricornus** is visible. Above Aquila, farther along the **Great Rift** is the small constellation of **Scutum**, with **M11**, the Wild Duck Cluster. To its east is the tiny, but distinctive constellation of **Delphinus**. Still farther along the Great Rift lies the centre of the Milky Way Galaxy (in **Sagittarius**) and, near it, two emission nebulae: **M8** (the Lagoon Nebula) and **M20** (the Trifid Nebula). In the western sky, the constellation of **Boötes** and **Arcturus** (α Boötis) are beginning to approach the horizon, but **Corona Borealis** is still clearly seen. Even farther west, the whole of **Virgo** is visible, with **Libra** above it. The large constellation of **Ophiuchus** and the two halves of **Serpens** lie between Hercules and the zenith. **Scorpius** is draped around the actual zenith with Sagittarius to its east.

The constellation of Virgo. Spica (α Virginis) is the bright blue star near the top of the image, with Mars to its northeast (south is up).

The Moon's phases for July

					First Quarter			
01	**02**	**03**	**04**	**05**	**06**	**07** 02:14	**08**	**09**
Day 3	Day 4	Day 5	Day 6	Day 7	Day 8	Day 9	Day 10	Day 11

			Full Moon				
10	**11**	**12**	**13** 18:38	**14**	**15**	**16**	
Day 12	Day 13	Day 14	Day 15	Day 16	Day 17	Day 18	

Last Quarter								
17	**18**	**19**	**20** 14:19	**21**	**22**	**23**	**24**	**25**
Day 19	Day 20	Day 21	Day 22	Day 23	Day 24	Day 25	Day 26	Day 27

		New Moon			
26	**27**	**28** 17:55	**29**	**30**	**31**
Day 28	Day 29	Day 30	Day 1	Day 2	Day 3

July – Moon and Planets

The Earth

The Earth reaches aphelion, the farthest point from the Sun in its yearly orbit, at 07:11 on July 4 at a distance of 1.016715374 AU (152,098,455.06 km).

The Moon

On July 3, the Moon, a waxing crescent, passes 4.9° north of **Regulus**, between it and **Algieba**. On July 7 in daylight, it is the same distance (4.9°) north of **Spica**. On July 11, two days before Full, it passes 3.0° north of **Antares**. On July 15, two days after Full Moon, it is 4.1° south of **Saturn** in **Capricornus**. By July 19, nearing Last Quarter, it is 2.2° south of **Jupiter**. On July 21 it is 1.1° north of **Mars**, and then, a day later, just 0.2° north of **Uranus**. The Moon is 7.4° north of **Aldebaran** on July 24. It is 4.2° north of **Venus** on July 26, and, the next day, is 2.2° south of **Pollux** in **Gemini**.

The planets

Mercury, initially in **Taurus**, rapidly moves towards the Sun and comes to superior conjunction on July 16. **Venus** is also initially in Taurus and is visible in the morning sky at mag. -3.9 to -3.8. **Mars** moves from **Pisces** into **Aries**, brightening slightly from mag. 0.5 to 0.2. **Jupiter** (mag. -2.4 to -2.6) on the border of **Pisces** and **Cetus**, begins retrograde motion late in the month (on July 29). **Saturn** (mag. 0.6 to 0.4) continues retrograde motion in **Capricornus**. **Uranus** is still in **Aries** at mag. 5.8, and **Neptune** is in **Pisces** at mag. 7.9.

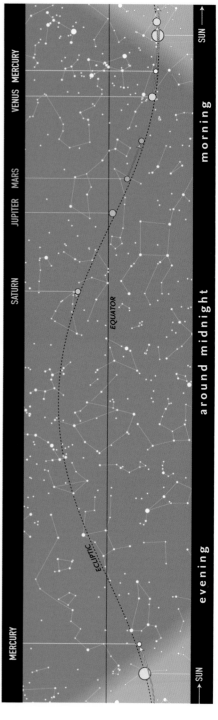

The path of the Sun and the planets along the ecliptic in July.

2	00:00 *	Venus 4.2°N of Aldebaran
3–Aug.15		α-Capricornid meteor shower
3	09:22	Regulus 4.9°S of Moon
4	07:11	Earth at aphelion
		(1.016715 AU = 152,098,455 km)
7	02:14	First Quarter
7	15:37	Spica 4.9°S of Moon
1	00:22	Antares 3.0°S of Moon
2–Aug.23		Southern δ-Aquariid meteor
		shower
3	09:06	Moon at perigee (closest of year)
		= 357,264 km
3	18:38	Full Moon
5–Aug.10		Piscis Austrinid meteor shower
5	20:17	Saturn 4.1°N of Moon
6	19:38	Mercury at superior conjunction
7–Aug.24		Perseid meteor shower
8	00:50	Neptune 3.3°N of Moon
9	00:59	Jupiter 2.2°N of Moon
0	14:19	Last Quarter
1	16:46	Mars 1.1°S of Moon
2	06:21	Uranus 0.2°S of Moon
4	03:36	Aldebaran 7.4°S of Moon
6	10:22	Moon at apogee = 406,273 km
6	14:11	Venus 4.2°S of Moon
7	18:21	Pollux 2.2°N of Moon
8		Piscis Austrinid meteor shower
		maximum
8	17:55	New Moon
9	21:07	Mercury 3.6°S of Moon
0		α-Capricornid meteor shower
		maximum
0		Southern δ-Aquariid meteor
		shower maximum
0	15:08	Regulus 4.8°S of Moon
		*These objects are close together for an extended
		period around this time.

Evening 7:30 p.m.

5

Denebola

4

3

Regulus •

Algieba

WNW

NW

10°

July 3–5 • In the northwest, the Moon passes between Regulus and Algieba and is close to Denebola on July 5.

Evening 9 p.m.

Cat's Eyes

11

Antares

Dschubba

10

Acrab

Sabik

ZENITH

N

10°

July 10–11 • In the north, and close to the zenith, the Moon passes Acrab (β Sco), Dschubba (δ Sco) and Antares. Sabik and the 'Cat's Eyes' are nearby.

Morning 6:30 a.m.

Betelgeuse

Alhena

Venus

25

Elnath

26

27

24

NE

10°

July 25–27 • The waning crescent Moon passes Elnath and Venus. Alhena and Betelgeuse are nearby.

Early morning 4 a.m.

CETUS

Uranus

Mars

22

22°

23

ARIES

5°

NE

July 22–23 • The Moon passes Mars and Uranus. Note the different scale (stars to mag. 5.5, Uranus is 5.8)

After midnight 1 a.m.

19

Jupiter

20

25°

10°

ENE

July 19–20 • After midnight, the Moon passes Jupiter in the east-northeast.

August 01   11 p.m.
August 15   10 p.m.

August – Looking South

Three inconspicuous constellations: *Volans*, *Chamaeleon* and *Octans* are on the meridian, with *Pavo* higher towards the zenith. Much of *Carina* is below the horizon, although the *Eta Carinae Nebula* and the *Southern Pleiades* are still visible. The *Large Magellanic Cloud* (LMC) and the faint constellation of *Mensa* are slightly higher in the sky. *Crux* is now lower, but the whole of *Centaurus* and *Lupus* remains visible. Much of *Virgo* has set in the west and *Libra* is following it down towards the horizon. *Scorpius* and *Sagittarius* are still visible high in the sky. *Achernar*, the *Small Magellanic Cloud* (SMC) and *Hydrus* are now well clear of the horizon, but below them are more small, inconspicuous constellations: *Dorado*, *Reticulum* and *Horlogium*. More of *Eridanus* is visible, together with parts of *Pictor* and *Fornax*. Much of *Cetus* has risen and the whole of the western arm of *Pisces* is now clearly seen. *Sculptor*, *Grus* and *Piscis Austrinus* lie half-way between the eastern horizon and the zenith, with faint *Microscopium* closer to the actual zenith.

Meteors

The *Piscis Austrinid* shower continues until about August 10, after maximum on July 28. The *Southern δ-Aquariids* reach maximum on July 30 to August 1, but are unlikely to exhibit more than about 20 meteors per hour. There are several minor southern showers active during the month: the *Northern δ-Aquariids* (maximum August 13), the *Southern* and *Northern ι-Aquariids* (maxima August 4 and August 19, respectively), but in all cases the rates are very low, just single figures per hour. The *α-Aurigid* shower begins on August 28, and is a short shower, lasting until September 5, reaching maximum in 2022 on September 1.

The Large Magellanic Cloud (LMC) lies mostly in the constellation of Dorado, partly extending into neighbouring Mensa. It contains many globular and open clusters as well as gaseous nebulae, such as the giant Tarantula Nebula.

August - Looking North

August – Looking North

Cygnus, with brilliant Deneb (α Cygni), is now prominent just to the east of the meridian. The other two stars of the (northern) Summer Triangle, **Vega** in **Lyra** and **Altair** in **Aquila** are also unmistakeable in the sky. **Hercules,** however, is beginning to descend towards the northwestern horizon. Above it, the sprawling constellation of **Ophiuchus** is readily seen. The Great Square of **Pegasus** is now visible in the east, although **Alpheratz** (α Andromedae) is low on the horizon. The western side of **Pisces, Aquarius** and **Capricornus** are fully visible along the ecliptic. **Sagittarius** contains many gaseous nebulae, like **M8** (the Lagoon Nebula) and **M20** (the Trifid Nebula) and several globular clusters such as **M22.** The constellation is at the zenith, with Scorpius to the west.

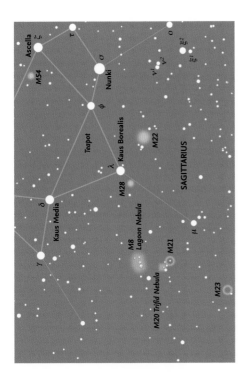

A finder chart for the gaseous nebulae M8 (the Lagoon Nebula), M20 (the Trifid Nebula) and the globular cluster M22, all in Sagittarius. Clusters M21, M23 (open) and M28 (globular) are faint. The chart shows all stars brighter than magnitude 7.5 (south is up).

The Moon's phases for August

August – Moon and Planets

The Moon

On August 3, the waxing crescent Moon passes 4.6° north of *Spica* in *Virgo*. On August 7, it passes 2.8° north of *Antares*. On August 12, at Full Moon, it is 3.9° south of *Saturn*. It passes 1.9° south of *Jupiter* on August 15 and 0.6° north of *Uranus* in *Aries* on August 18. Just after Last Quarter on August 19, it is 2.7° north of *Mars* in *Taurus*, having passed the *Pleiades*. The next day, it passes 7.6° north of *Aldebaran*. On August 24, the waning crescent is 2.1° south of *Pollux*. The following day it passes 4.3° north of *Venus*. On August 26, one day before New Moon, the narrow crescent passes 4.7° north of *Regulus*. By August 31, the waxing crescent is 4.4° north of *Spica* in *Virgo*.

The planets

Mercury is low in the twilight. It comes to greatest elongation (27.3°) east at mag. 0.2, on August 27. *Venus* (mag. -3.8 to -3.9), initially in *Gemini*, rapidly moves towards the Sun and into twilight. *Mars* moves from *Aries* (at mag. 0.2) into *Taurus*, brightening to mag. -0.1. *Jupiter*, just within the top of *Cetus*, continues slow retrograde motion, slowly increasing from mag. -2.7 to mag. -2.9 over the month. *Saturn* is at opposition (mag. 0.3) in *Capricornus* on August 14. *Uranus* is still in *Aries* at mag. 5.8, and begins retrograde motion on August 25. *Neptune* retrogrades from *Pisces* into *Aquarius* at mag. 7.9. On August 22, minor planet (4) *Vesta* is at opposition in *Aquarius* at mag. 5.8 (see chart on page 26).

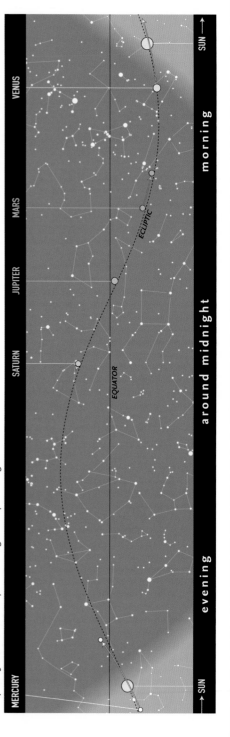

The path of the Sun and the planets along the ecliptic in August.

Calendar for August

1	09:00 *	Uranus 1.4°N of Mars
3	22:01	Spica 4.6°S of Moon
5	11:06	First Quarter
7	09:02	Antares 2.8°S of Moon
7	10:00 *	Venus 6.6°S of Pollux
0	17:09	Moon at perigee = 359,828 km
2–13		Perseid meteor shower maximum
2	01:36	Full Moon
2	03:56	Saturn 3.9°N of Moon
4	09:53	Neptune 3.1°N of Moon
4	17:10	Saturn at opposition (mag. 0.3)
5	09:42	Jupiter 1.9°N of Moon
8	14:38	Uranus 0.6°S of Moon
9	04:36	Last Quarter
9	12:17	Mars 2.7°S of Moon
0	10:24	Aldebaran 7.6°S of Moon
2	18:55	Minor planet (4) Vesta at opposition (mag. 5.8)
2	21:52	Moon at apogee = 405,418 km
4	00:53	Pollux 2.1°N of Moon
5	20:57	Venus 4.3°S of Moon
6	21:25	Regulus 4.7°S of Moon
7	08:17	New Moon
7	16:14	Mercury at greatest elongation (27.3°E, mag. 0.2)
8–Sep.05		α-Aurigid meteor shower
9	10:51	Mercury 6.6°S of Moon
1	03:35	Spica 4.4°S of Moon

These objects are close together for an extended period of time

Morning 6:30 a.m.

August 7 • *Shortly before sunrise, Venus is close to Castor and Pollux, which will probably be lost in twilight. Alhena and Procyon are nearby.*

Early morning 3 a.m.

August 2 • *Mars is close to Uranus (mag. 5.8). The faintest stars shown here are of magnitude 5.5. Note the different scale of this illustration.*

Evening 6:30 p.m.

August 31 • *High in the west, Spica is in the company of the waxing crescent Moon.*

Morning 6 a.m.

August 19–21 • *The Last Quarter Moon passes Mars, the Pleiades and Aldebaran, almost due north.*

Morning 6 a.m.

August 15–16 • *The Moon passes Jupiter in the west-northwest. Diphda (β Cet) is higher in the sky*

September, Looking South

September 01   11 p.m.
September 15   10 p.m.

September – Looking South

The smallest of the constellations, **Crux**, is now very low, but **Canopus** (α Carinae), the second brightest star in the sky, has now become visible once more. **Dorado** and the **Large Magellanic Cloud** (LMC) are higher and easier to see, as are the faint constellations of **Pictor, Caelum** and **Reticulum**. The **Small Magellanic Cloud** (SMC) and **47 Tucanae** are now nearly half-way between the horizon and the zenith. Although becoming low, the whole of **Centaurus** and **Lupus** remains visible in the southwest. **Scorpius** with reddish **Antares** is beginning to descend in the west, but **Sagittarius** is clearly seen high in the sky. The constellation of **Piscis Austrinus**, with **Fomalhaut** (α Piscis Austrini), is at the zenith. Below it are the constellations of **Grus** and **Pavo**, with **Achernar** (α Eridani) and almost the whole of the long constellation of **Eridanus.**

Meteors

There are no major meteor showers active in September. A few meteors may be seen from the **α-Aurigid** shower, active from late August, with possible maximum on September 1. The **Southern Taurid** shower begins this month (on September 10) and, although rates are low (less than 6 per hour), often produces very bright fireballs. This is a very long shower, lasting until about November 20. There is one minor shower, the **Piscids**, active throughout September with a slight maximum on September 19, but with an overall rate of no more than 3–5 meteors per hour. However, September is notable for a considerable increase in the number of sporadic meteors, which are, of course, completely unpredictable in location, direction and magnitude.

The 'Teapot' of Sagittarius at the top of the image with the curl of stars forming Corona Australis in the lower left, and the 'Cat's Eyes' (Shaula and Leseth) in the 'sting' of Scorpius near the right edge of the image. The bright open cluster M7 (in Scorpius) is prominent between Sagittarius and the Cat's Eyes (north is up).

September – Looking North

The Great Square of **Pegasus** is nearing the meridian from the east and, on the west, the three bright stars of the Northern Summer Triangle, **Deneb** (α Cygni), **Altair** (α Aquilae) and **Vega** (α Lyrae) are still clearly seen, although Vega is low on the horizon, as is **M31** in **Andromeda**. **Delphinus** is well-placed, as are the fainter constellation of **Sagitta** and **Scutum** along the Milky Way. Giant **Ophiuchus** is beginning to descend towards the western horizon and much of **Libra** has disappeared. The three zodiacal constellations of **Pisces**, **Aquarius** and **Capricornus** are readily visible. Somewhat higher, **Piscis Austrinus** and **Fomalhaut** (α Piscis Austrini) is at the zenith. **Scorpius** and **Sagittarius** are now on the western side of the sky.

The constellation of Aquarius is one of the constellations that is visible in late winter and early spring. The four stars forming the 'Y'-shape of the 'Water Jar' may be seen to the east (right) of Sadalmelik (α Aquarii), the brightest star near the bottom centre (south is up).

The Moon's phases for September

Last Quarter
First Quarter

| 01 | 02 | 03 18:08 | 04 | 05 | 06 | 07 | 08 | 09 |
| Day 6 | Day 7 | Day 8 | Day 9 | Day 10 | Day 11 | Day 12 | Day 13 | Day 14 |

Full Moon

| 10 09:59 | 11 | 12 | 13 | 14 | 15 | 16 |
| Day 15 | Day 16 | Day 17 | Day 18 | Day 19 | Day 20 | Day 21 |

New Moon

| 17 21:52 | 18 | 19 | 20 | 21 | 22 | 23 | 24 | 25 21:55 |
| Day 22 | Day 23 | Day 24 | Day 25 | Day 26 | Day 27 | Day 28 | Day 29 | Day 30 |

| 26 | 27 | 28 | 29 | 30 |
| Day 1 | Day 2 | Day 3 | Day 4 | Day 5 |

September – Moon and Planets

The Earth

The Sun crosses the celestial equator at the southern spring equinox at 01:04 on Friday, September 23. Day length changes most rapidly at the equinoxes. In the southern hemisphere, the greatest increase is in September and the most rapid decrease in March.

The Moon

The First Quarter Moon is 2.5° north of *Antares* in *Scorpius* on September 3. On September 8, the Moon passes 3.9° south of *Saturn*. On September 11, one day past Full, the Moon is 1.8° south of *Jupiter*. Just before Last Quarter, the Moon is 3.6° north of *Mars* on September 17. On September 20, the Moon is 1.9° south of *Pollux* in *Gemini*. The Moon is close to *Venus* on September 25, low in the morning twilight.

On September 30, the Moon again passes (2.3° north) of *Antares* as it did at the beginning of the month.

The planets

Mercury is close to the Sun, and comes to inferior conjunction on September 23. Venus is also close to the Sun, but may be glimpsed in morning twilight later in the month. *Mars* is moving eastwards in *Taurus*, brightening from mag. -0.1 to mag. -0.6 over the month. *Jupiter* (mag. -2.9) comes to opposition on September 26. *Saturn* remains in *Capricornus* at mag. 0.4 to 0.5. *Uranus* remains in *Aries* at mag. 5.8, and *Neptune* is in *Aquarius* at mag. 7.8, coming to opposition on September 16. On September 7, minor planet (3)*Juno* is at opposition at mag. 7.9 (see chart on page 27).

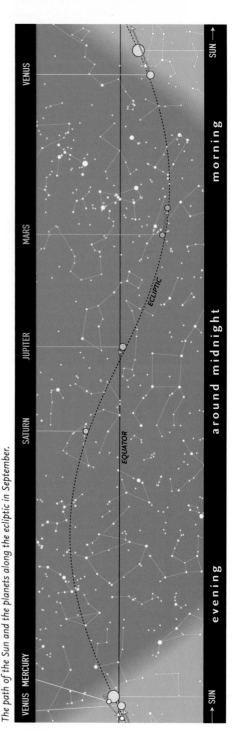

The path of the Sun and the planets along the ecliptic in September.

01		α-Aurigid meteor shower maximum
03	15:29	Antares 2.5°S of Moon
03	18:08	First Quarter
05	01:00 *	Venus is 0.8°N of Regulus
07	16:49	Minor planet (3) Juno at opposition (mag. 7.9)
07	18:19	Moon at perigee = 364,492 km
08	10:31	Saturn 3.9°N of Moon
09	01:00 *	Mars 4.3°N of Aldebaran
10–Nov.20		Southern Taurid meteor shower
10	09:59	Full Moon
10	18:54	Neptune 3.0°N of Moon
11	15:17	Jupiter 1.8°N of Moon
14	22:59	Uranus 0.8°S of Moon
16	18:19	Aldebaran 7.8°S of Moon
16	22:21	Neptune at opposition (mag. 7.8)
17	01:43	Mars 3.6°S of Moon
17	21:52	Last Quarter
19	14:43	Moon at apogee = 404,556 km
20	08:17	Pollux 1.9°N of Moon
23	01:04	Southern spring equinox
23	04:51	Regulus 4.8°S of Moon
23	06:50	Mercury at inferior conjunction
25		New Zealand Daylight Saving Time begins
25	05:08	Venus 2.8°S of Moon
25	08:14	Mercury 6.7°S of Moon
25	21:55	New Moon
26	19:33	Jupiter at opposition (mag. −2.9)
27	09:57	Spica 4.2°S of Moon
30	20:53	Antares 2.3°S of Moon

These objects are close together for an extended

Evening 11 p.m.

Antares · Dschubba · Acrab — WSW — 10°

September 3 • *The Moon is close to Antares, with Acrab (β Sco) and Dschubba (δ Sco) right below it.*

After midnight 1 a.m.

55° · Jupiter — N — 10°

September 12 • *High in the north, the Moon is less than two degrees above Jupiter.*

After midnight 2 a.m.

Pleiades · 16 · Aldebaran · 17 · Mars · 18 · Elnath — NE — 10°

September 16–18 • *The Moon passes the Pleiades, Aldebaran and Mars. On September 18 it is close to Elnath.*

Morning 5 a.m.

Pollux · Castor — NNE · NE — 10°

September 20 • *Low in the northeast, the Moon forms an isosceles triangle with Castor and Pollux*

Evening 10 p.m.

Oct 1 · Antares · Sabik · Sep 30 · Acrab · Dschubba — WSW · W — 10°

September 30–October 1 • *The Moon visits Acrab, Dschubba, and Antares for the second time this month*

October – Looking South

Crux is now extremely low, only just visible above the horizon. The **False Cross** has reappeared, also very low, farther towards the east on the opposite side of the meridian. **Canopus** (α Carinae) is now much higher as is the **Large Magellanic Cloud** (LMC). The **Small Magellanic Cloud** (SMC) and the globular cluster **47 Tucanae** are on the southern meridian, half-way to the zenith as is **Achernar** (α Eridani). (The whole of the long constellation of **Eridanus** is now visible together with **Rigel** in **Orion**.) Still higher are **Phoenix**, **Grus** and **Piscis Austrinus**. **Pavo** has begun to descend in the southwest. **Ophiuchus** has now slipped below the horizon as has much of **Scorpius**, only the 'tail' of which remains visible. **Sagittarius** is getting lower, but remains visible, as do the zodiacal constellations of **Capricornus** and **Aquarius**.

Meteors

The **Orionids** are the major, fairly reliable meteor shower active in October. Like the May **η-Aquariid** shower, the Orionids are associated with Comet 1P/Halley. During this second pass through the stream of particles from the comet, slightly fewer meteors are seen than in May. In both showers the meteors are very fast, and many leave persistent trains. Although the Orionid maximum is nominally October 21–22, in fact there is a very broad maximum, lasting about a week from October 20 to 27, with hourly rates around 25. Occasionally, rates are higher (50–70 per hour). In 2022, the Moon is a waning crescent, so conditions are reasonably favourable.

The faint shower of the **Southern Taurids** (often with bright fireballs) peaks on October 10. The Southern Taurid maximum occurs one day after Full Moon, so conditions are extremely unfavourable. Towards the end of the month (around October 20), another shower (the Northern Taurids) begins to show activity, which peaks early in November. The combined radiants for both Taurid showers are close together. The combined position is shown on the 'Looking North' chart. The parent comet for both Taurid showers is Comet 2P/Encke.

The Small Magellanic Cloud, one of the satellite galaxies of the Milky Way. Near the right edge of this image is 47 Tucanae (NGC 104), which is the second brightest globular cluster in the sky, after Omega Centauri (see page 53). North is up.

October 01   11 p.m.   (12 p.m. NZDT)
October 15   10 p.m.   (11 p.m. DST)

October – Looking North

The Great Square of **Pegasus** now dominates the sky to the north and the whole of **Andromeda** with the **Andromeda Galaxy** (M31) is now clear of the horizon. The two chains of stars forming **Pisces** frame the Great Square and, farther along the ecliptic, the constellations of **Aquarius** and **Capricornus** are fully visible. Farther east, all of **Cetus** is visible and, low down on the horizon, **Aldebaran** in **Taurus** is beginning to rise. Due east, **Orion** is becoming visible, with blue-white **Rigel** and the beginning of the long, winding constellation of **Eridanus** that wends its way to **Achernar** (α Eridani), far to the south. West of the meridian, **Lyra**, with **Vega** has disappeared; much of **Cygnus** is invisible and **Deneb** is brushing the horizon. Only **Aquila** and **Altair** (α Aquilae) remain clearly visible. **Vulpecula**, with the planetary nebula **M27** is still visible as is **Sagitta** and, above them, the distinctive constellation of **Delphinus** and the very faint, inconspicuous constellation of **Equuleus**.

The Great Square of Pegasus. The star at the northeastern corner (at the right) is Alpheratz (α Andromedae) and is actually part of the constellation of Andromeda (south is up).

The Moon's phases for October

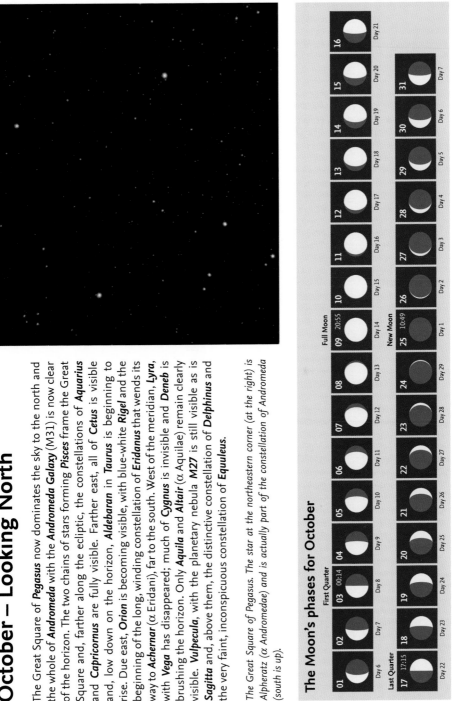

October – Moon and Planets

The Moon

On October 8, one day before Full Moon, it is 2.1° south of **Jupiter** in **Pisces**. It passes 0.9° north of **Uranus** (mag. 5.7) in **Aries** on October 12. Waning gibbous, it passes **Aldebaran** on October 14, and is 3.6° north of **Mars** the next day. At Last Quarter, on October 17, it is 1.8° south of **Pollux**. As a waning crescent, on October 20 it is 4.9° north of **Regulus**, between it and **Algieba**. It is 4.2° north of **Spica** on October 24, and at New Moon, the next day, there is a partial solar eclipse (see page 20). The waxing crescent is 2.3° north of **Antares** on October 28.

The planets

Mercury is at greatest elongation west at mag. -0.6 on October 8, low in the morning sky. **Venus** is close to the Sun, and comes to superior conjunction on October 22. It is occulted by the Moon on October 25, but the event occurs in daylight. **Mars**, in **Taurus**, brightens from mag. -0.6 to mag. -1.2 over the month. It begins retrograde motion on October 31. **Jupiter**, after opposition in September, is still retrograding in **Pisces** at mag. -2.9 to -2.8. **Saturn** is retrograding slowly in **Capricornus** and resumes direct motion on October 23. **Uranus** (mag. 5.7) is in **Aries**, and **Neptune** (mag. 7.8) is in **Aquarius**.

The path of the Sun and the planets along the ecliptic in October.

Calendar for October

02–Nov.07		Orionid meteor shower
02		Australian Daylight Saving Time begins
03	00:14	First Quarter
04	16:34	Moon at perigee = 369,325 km
05	15:51	Saturn 4.1°N of Moon
08	02:33	Neptune 3.1°N of Moon
08	18:12	Jupiter 2.1°N of Moon
08	21:14	Mercury at greatest elongation (18.0°W, mag. -0.6)
09	20:55	Full Moon
10–11		Southern Taurid meteor shower maximum
12	06:46	Uranus 0.9°S of Moon
14	02:56	Aldebaran 8.0°S of Moon
15	04:31	Mars 3.6°S of Moon
17	10:20	Moon at apogee = 404,328 km
17	16:19	Pollux 1.8°N of Moon
17	17:15	Last Quarter
20–Dec.10		Northern Taurid meteor shower
20	13:17	Regulus 4.9°S of Moon
21–22		Orionid meteor shower maximum
22	21:17	Venus at superior conjunction
24	15:44	Mercury 0.4°S of Moon
24	18:14	Spica 4.2°S of Moon
25	10:49	New Moon
25	11:00	Partial solar eclipse
25	12:05	Venus occultation
28	03:21	Antares 2.3°S of Moon
29	14:36	Moon at perigee = 368,291 km

Evening 8 p.m. (DST)

October 8–9 • The nearly Full Moon passes Jupiter in the eastern sky. Diphda (β Cet) is due east.

Morning 5 a.m. (DST)

October 14–16 • The waning gibbous Moon passes the Pleiades, Aldebaran, Mars and Elnath. Alhena is a little farther northeast.

Early morning 4 a.m. (DST)

October 18 • The Last Quarter Moon is close to Castor and Pollux, with both Alhena and Procyon about 15° higher in the sky.

Morning 5:30 a.m. (DST)

October 21 • The waning crescent Moon is between Regulus and Algieba, low in the northeastern sky.

TAURUS

MARS

ORION

Betelgeuse

M42 Orion Nebula

Rigel

ERIDANUS

Sirius

CANIS MAJOR

Adhara

MONOCEROS

LEPUS

CAELUM

COLUMBA

Canopus

PUPPIS

PYXIS

ANT

VELA

False Cross

Eta Carinae Nebula

CARINA

PICTOR

DORADO

Tarantula Nebula

LMC

RETICULUM

HOROLOGIUM

FORNAX

ZENITH

CETUS

SCULPTOR

Achernar

PHOENIX

HYDRUS

MENSA

VOLANS

CHAMAELEON

Southern Pleiades

CEN

CRUX

Acrux

Mimosa

Jewel Box

Coalsack

MUSCA

Hadar

CEN

Rigil Kentaurus

CIRCINUS

NORMA

SCORPIUS

ARA

TELESCOPIUM

CORONA AUSTRALIS

SAGITTARIUS

Kaus Australis

Nunki

TRIANGULUM AUSTRALE

APUS

OCTANS

South Celestial Pole

SMC

47 Tucanae

TUCANA

GRUS

PAVO

Peacock

INDUS

MICROSCOPIUM

PISCIS AUSTRINUS

Fomalhaut

AQUARIUS

Water Jar

CAPRICORNUS

SATURN

ECLIPTIC

PEGASUS

EQUULEUS

M15

AQUILA

S

E

November 01   11 p.m.   (12 p.m. DST)
November 15   10 p.m.   (11 p.m. DST)

November – Looking South

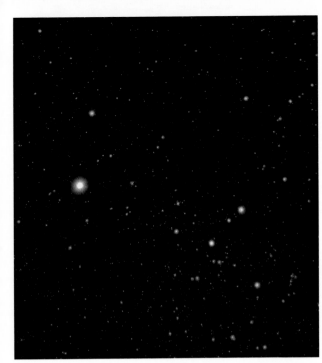

The constellation of Canis Major, with Sirius, the brightest star in the sky (mag. –1,4) in the upper half of the image. Below Sirius is the open cluster M41 (north is up).

Crux and the two brightest stars of **Centaurus, Rigil Kentaurus** (α Centauri) and **Hadar** (β Centauri), are extremely low on the southern horizon. The **False Cross** on the **Carina/Vela** border is now higher, and the constellation of **Puppis** as well as **Canopus** (α Carinae) and both the **Large Magellanic Cloud** (LMC) and the **Small Magellanic Cloud** (SMC) are clearly visible. **Achernar** (α Eridani) is half-way between the South Celestial Pole and the zenith. The whole of **Eridanus**, which starts near **Rigel** in **Orion**, is now clearly seen as it winds its way to Achernar. **Pavo** is becoming lower in the southwest, and in the west, most of **Sagittarius** is below the horizon, with **Capricornus** descending behind it. **Corona Australis** is still just visible. In the east, **Canis Major** is now clearly seen, together with the small constellations of **Columba** and **Lepus** above it.

Meteors

Two meteor showers begin in September or October but continue into November. The **Orionids** (see page 89), one of the streams associated with Comet 1/P Halley, continue until about November 7. The **Southern Taurids** (see page 83) begin on September 10 and continue until November 20. Because of the location of the radiant, the **Leonid** shower is best seen from the northern hemisphere, but southern observers may see some rising from the horizon. They have a short period of activity (November 6–30), with maximum on November 17–18. This shower is associated with Comet 55P/Tempel-Tuttle and has shown extraordinary activity on various occasions with many thousands of meteors per hour. The rate in 2022 is likely to be about 15 per hour. These meteors are the fastest shower meteors recorded (about 70 km per second) and often leave persistent trains. The shower is very rich in faint meteors.

There is a minor southern meteor shower that begins activity in late November (nominally November 28). This is the **Phoenicids**, but little is known of the shower, partly because the parent comet is believed to be the disintegrated comet D/1819 W1 (Blanpain). With no accurate knowledge of the location of the remnants of the comet, predicting the possible rate becomes little more than guesswork, but the rate is variable and may rapidly increase (as might be expected) if the orbit is nearby. Bright meteors tend to be quite frequent and the meteors are fairly slow. The radiant is located within Phoenix, not far from the border with **Eridanus** and the bright star **Achernar** (α Eridani).

November 01   11 p.m.   (12 p.m. DST)
November 15   10 p.m.   (11 p.m. DST)

November — Looking North

November – Looking North

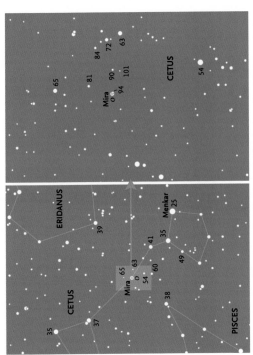

Andromeda is now due north, and the **Andromeda Galaxy** (M31) has risen sufficiently to be clearly seen. The constellation of *Triangulum* lies between Andromeda and the zodiacal constellation of *Aries*. Much of *Perseus* (including the variable star, **Algol**) is now above the horizon, together with part of **Auriga**. The whole of *Pegasus*, with the **Great Square**, is clearly seen and, above it the two lines of stars forming *Pisces* and the distinctive asterism of the **Circlet**. Higher still is the constellation of *Cetus* with the famous variable star, **Mira**. The whole of *Taurus* with **Aldebaran** (α Tauri), and the **Pleiades** and the **Hyades** clusters are visible in the southeast. **Orion** has fully risen in the east with **Lepus** above it. The long, winding constellation of **Eridanus** begins near **Rigel** in Orion. The faint constellation of *Monoceros* lies to the east of Orion and straddles the Milky Way. **Canis Major** and brilliant **Sirius** are even farther round towards the east. In the west, the zodiacal constellations of **Aquarius** (with its distinctive asterism of the **Water Jar**) and **Capricornus** are clearly seen, with **Piscis Austrinus** and bright **Fomalhaut** (α Piscis Austrini) higher in the sky. The faint constellation of **Sculptor** lies between Piscis Austrinus and the zenith.

Finder and comparison charts for Mira (o Ceti). The chart on the left shows all stars brighter than magnitude 6.5. The chart on the right shows stars down to magnitude 10.0. The comparison star magnitudes are shown without the decimal point (south is up).

The Moon's phases for November

November – Moon and Planets

The Moon

Just after First Quarter on November 1, the Moon is 4.2° south of **Venus**, **Saturn**. On November 4 it is 2.4° south of **Jupiter** in Pisces. There is a total lunar eclipse at Full Moon on November 8 (see page 20). The Moon is 8.0° north of **Aldebaran** on November 10 and is 2.5° north of **Mars** in **Taurus** the next day. The Moon is 1.7° south of **Pollux** on November 14. Just after Last Quarter, on November 16, the Moon is 5.0° north of **Regulus.** On November 21 it is 4.2° north of **Spica** in **Virgo.** On November 29, it again passes 4.2° south of Saturn, as it did on November 1.

The planets

Mercury comes to superior conjunction on November 8. **Venus,** although bright (mag. -4.0 to -3.9) is lost in twilight, close to the Sun. **Mars**, which began retrograde motion on October 31, is in **Taurus,** brightening from mag. -1.2 to -1.8 over the month. **Jupiter** (mag. -2.8 to -2.6), initially retrograding in **Pisces,** resumes direct motion on November 26. **Saturn** (mag. 0.7 to 0.8) is moving slowly eastwards in **Capricornus. Uranus,** in **Aries** at mag. 5.6 is at opposition on November 9. **Neptune** is in **Aquarius** at mag. 7.8 to 7.9.

The path of the Sun and the planets along the ecliptic in November.

Calendar for November

01	06:37	First Quarter
01	21:08	Saturn 4.2°N of Moon
04	08:20	Neptune 3.2°N of Moon
04	20:24	Jupiter 2.4°N of Moon
06–30		Leonid meteor shower
08	10:58	Total lunar eclipse
08	11:02	Full Moon
08	13:11	Uranus 0.8°S of Moon
08	16:43	Mercury at superior conjunction
09	08:26	Uranus at opposition (mag. 5.6)
10	11:22	Aldebaran 8.0°S of Moon
11	13:46	Mars 2.5°S of Moon
12–13		Northern Taurid meteor shower maximum
14	00:20	Pollux 1.7°N of Moon
14	06:40	Moon at apogee = 404,921 km
16	13:27	Last Quarter
16	21:53	Regulus 5.0°S of Moon
17–18		Leonid meteor shower maximum
21	04:11	Spica 4.2°S of Moon
23	22:57	New Moon
24	12:18	Antares 2.3°S of Moon
24	14:02	Venus 2.3°N of Moon
24	15:03	Mercury 0.9°N of Moon
26	01 31	Moon at perigee = 362,826 km
28–Dec.09		Phoenicid meteor shower
29	04:40	Saturn 4.2°N of Moon
30	14:36	First Quarter

Evening 8 p.m. (DST)

Saturn • Fomalhaut • 2 • 3 • 4 • 5 • Jupiter • 65° • 10° • N • NNE • NE

November 2–5 • *The waxing gibbous Moon passes Saturn and Jupiter, high in the northeastern sky. Fomalhaut is even higher.*

After midnight 0:30 a.m. (DST)

Bellatrix • 30° • NE • Aldebaran • Mars • 12 • Elnath • 11 • Pléiades • 10 • 10° • NNE

November 10–12 • *The Moon passes the Pleiades, Aldebaran, Elnath and Mars. Bellatrix (γ Ori) is a little higher and due northeast.*

Morning 5 a.m. (DST)

Pollux • Castor • 10° • N

November 14 • *Almost due north, the Moon is in the company of Castor and Pollux.*

Morning 5 a.m. (DST)

Spica • 21 • 22 • 10° • E

November 21–22 • *The waxing crescent Moon passes Spica, in the early morning.*

Evening 10 p.m. (DST)

Saturn • 35° • 10° • W

November 29 • *For the second time this month, the Moon is close to Saturn.*

PEGASUS

Circlet

PISCES

ECLIPTIC

Water Jar

AQUARIUS

JUPITER

SATURN

CETUS

PISCIS AUSTRINUS

CAPRICORNUS

SCULPTOR

Fomalhaut

GRUS

MICROSCOPIUM

FORNAX

PHOENIX

Phoenicids

INDUS

SAGITTARIUS

ZENITH

ERIDANUS

HOROLOGIUM

Achernar

RETICULUM

47 Tucanae

SMC

TUCANA

PAVO

Peacock

TELESCOPIUM

CAELUM

DORADO

LMC

HYDRUS

OCTANS

APUS

ARA

COLUMBA

Tarantula Nebula

MENSA

VOLANS

CHAMAELEON

South Celestial Pole

TRIANGULUM AUSTRALE

LEPUS

PICTOR

Southern Pleiades

MUSCA

Rigil Kentaurus

Rigel

Canopus

Eta Carinae Nebula

Acrux

Coalsack

Hadar

CIRCINUS

M42 Orion Nebula

CARINA

CRUX

Jewel Box

Mimosa

S

ORION

Puppid-Velids

False Cross

CENTAURUS

Adhara

PUPPIS

VELA

CANIS MAJOR

Sirius

ANTLIA

MONOCEROS

PYXIS

Procyon

CANIS MINOR

Alphard

Pollux

HYDRA

CANCER

E

ECLIPTIC

December. Looking South

December 01   11 p.m.   (12 p.m. DST)
December 15   10 p.m.   (11 p.m. DST)

December – Looking South

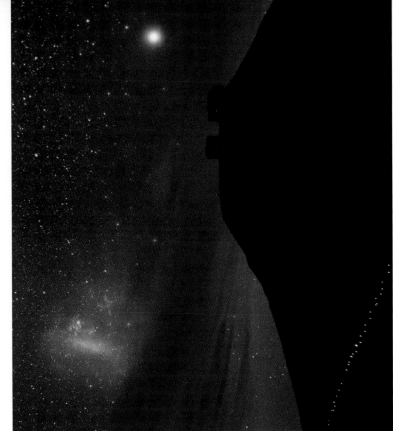

The Large Magellanic Cloud seen over the European Southern Observatory at Paranal in Chile. Brilliant Canopus (α Carinae), the second brightest star in the southern hemisphere, is visible through the low cloud to the right.

Crux and the two brightest stars in **Centaurus**, **Hadar** and **Rigil Kentaurus**, are now higher above the horizon. The **Eta Carina Nebula** and the **Southern Pleiades** are now conveniently placed for observation. Above them, the **False Cross** is clearly seen, with the whole of **Vela** and below it the inconspicuous constellation of **Antlia**. **Carina** with **Canopus** (α Carinae) and **Puppis** are roughly halfway between the horizon and the zenith. **Sirius** and **Canis Major** are high in the east. In the west, **Achernar** (α Eridani) and **Phoenix** are about the same altitude as Canopus. The faint constellations of **Pictor, Dorado, Reticulum** and **Horlogium** lie between them. **Pavo** with **Peacock** (α Pavonis) is becoming low, as are the constellations of **Indus, Grus** and **Piscis Austrinus**. Higher still are the inconspicuous constellations of **Sculptor** and, near the zenith, **Fornax**. **Capricornus** is largely invisible, but most of **Aquarius** may still be seen.

Meteors

The **Phoenicid** shower continues into December, reaching its weak maximum on December 2. The **Puppid Velid** shower's radiant is on the border between the two constellations. The shower begins on December 1, lasting until December 15, with maximum on December 7. It is a weak shower with a maximum hourly rate of about 10 meteors, but bright meteors are often seen. One of the most dependable showers of the year is the **Geminids**, active from December 4 to 20, with maximum in 2022 on December 14–15. The rate is often 60–70 per hour, and may rise even higher.

December 01   11 p.m.   (12 p.m. DST)
December 15   10 p.m.   (11 p.m. DST)

December – Looking North

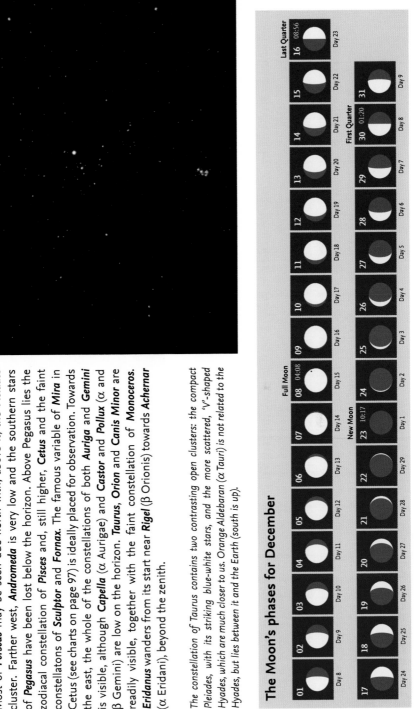

Most of **Perseus** may be seen due north with, above it, the **Pleiades** cluster. Farther west, **Andromeda** is very low and the southern stars of **Pegasus** have been lost below the horizon. Above Pegasus lies the zodiacal constellation of **Pisces** and, still higher, **Cetus** and the faint constellatons of **Sculptor** and **Fornax**. The famous variable of **Mira** in Cetus (see charts on page 97) is ideally placed for observation. Towards the east, the whole of the constellations of both **Auriga** and **Gemini** is visible, although **Capella** (α Aurigae) and **Castor** and **Pollux** (α and β Gemini) are low on the horizon. **Taurus**, **Orion** and **Canis Minor** are readily visible, together with the faint constellation of **Monoceros**. **Eridanus** wanders from its start near **Rigel** (β Orionis) towards **Achernar** (α Eridani), beyond the zenith.

The constellation of Taurus contains two contrasting open clusters: the compact Pleiades, with its striking blue-white stars, and the more scattered, 'V'-shaped Hyades, which are much closer to us. Orange Aldebaran (α Tauri) is not related to the Hyades, but lies between it and the Earth (south is up).

The Moon's phases for December

December – Moon and Planets

The Moon

On December 2, the Moon (waxing gibbous) is 2.5° south of **Jupiter** in **Pisces**. On December 8, a few minutes after Full Moon, it occults **Mars** (at opposition) in **Taurus**. The waning gibbous Moon passes 1.8° south of **Pollux** on December 11. On December 14 it passes 4.8° north of **Regulus**, between it and **Algieba**. On December 18 the Moon is 4.1° North of **Spica** in **Virgo**. On December 21, shortly before New Moon, it is 2.3° north of **Antares**. On December 24 it passes just south of both **Mercury** and **Venus**, but is so low it is probably lost in twilight. On December 26 it passes 4.0° south of **Saturn** in **Capricornus** and, on December 29, again 2.3° south of **Jupiter** as it was early in the month.

The planets

Mercury reaches greatest elongation east in the evening sky (20.1°, mag. -0.6) on December 21. **Venus** (mag. -3.9) becomes visible in the evening sky later in the month. **Mars** is in **Taurus** and comes to opposition on December 8 at mag. -1.9, when it is also occulted by the Full Moon. Although conditions will be difficult, the occultation should be visible from Western Europe and practically the whole of North America. **Jupiter** (mag. -2.6 to -2.4) is moving eastwards (direct motion) in **Pisces**. **Saturn** is in **Capricornus** at mag. 0.8. **Uranus** is still retrograding in **Aries**, and fades very slightly to mag. 5.7 at the end of the year. **Neptune** remains in **Aquarius** at mag. 7.6, but resumes direct motion on December 26.

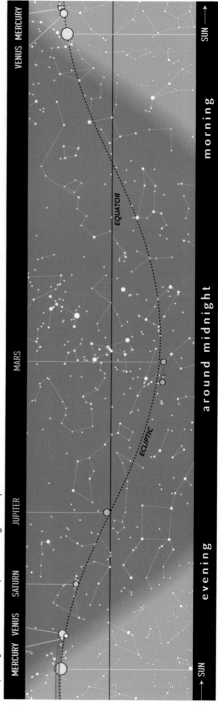

The path of the Sun and the planets along the ecliptic in December.

Calendar for December

Morning 5 a.m. (DST)

Regulus · 15 · 14 · Algieba · Denebola

December 14–15 • *The Moon with Regulus and Algieba high in the north. Denebola is farther northeast.*

Early morning 4 a.m. (DST)

Aldebaran · 9 · Elnath · Mars · 8

December 8–9 • *Low in the northwest, the Moon passes Aldebaran, Mars and Elnath.*

Evening 11 p.m. (DST)

Jupiter

December 29 • *Near the west, the Moon is close to Jupiter.*

Evening 8:40 p.m. (DST)

Venus · Mercury

December 29 • *Venus and Mercury are close together low in the west-southwest.*

Evening 8:30 p.m. (DST)

Nunki · 24 · Mercury · Venus · 25

December 24–25 • *The crescent Moon passes Venus and Mercury. Nunki is probably lost in twilight.*

Dark Sky Sites

International Dark-Sky Association Sites

The *International Dark-Sky Association* (IDA) recognizes various categories of sites that offer areas where the sky is dark at night, free from light pollution and particularly suitable for astonomical observing. Although a number of sites are under consideration, the majority of confirmed sites are in North America. There are at least 65 in the United States and Canada. There are 18 sites in Great Britain and Ireland, seven in Europe, and one each in Israel, Japan and South Korea. There are just 10 sites in the southern hemisphere.

Details of IDA are at: https://www.darksky.org/. Information on the various categories and individual sites are at:
https://www.darksky.org/our-work/conservation/idsp/.

Many of these sites have major observatories or other facilities available for public observing (often at specific dates or times).

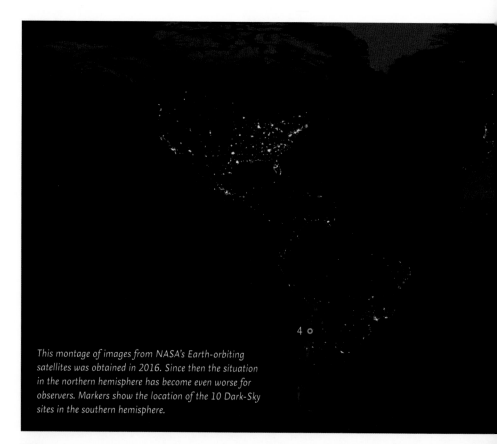

This montage of images from NASA's Earth-orbiting satellites was obtained in 2016. Since then the situation in the northern hemisphere has become even worse for observers. Markers show the location of the 10 Dark-Sky sites in the southern hemisphere.

1 *!Ae!Hai Kalahari Heritage Park* (South Africa)

2 *Aoraki Mackenzie* (New Zealand)

3 *Aotea / Great Barrier Island* (New Zealand)

4 *Gabriela Mistral* (Chile)

5 *NamibRand Nature Reserve* (Namibia)

6 *River Murray* (Australia)

7 *Stewart Island / Rakiura* (New Zealand)

8 *The Jump-Up* (Australia)

9 *Wai-Iti* (New Zealand)

10 *Warrumbungle National Park* (Australia)

Glossary and Tables

aphelion	The point on an orbit that is farthest from the Sun.
apogee	The point on its orbit at which the Moon is farthest from the Earth.
appulse	The apparently close approach of two celestial objects; two planets, or a planet and star.
astronomical unit	(AU) The mean distance of the Earth from the Sun, 149,597,870 km.
celestial equator	The great circle on the celestial sphere that is in the same plane as the Earth's equator.
celestial sphere	The apparent sphere surrounding the Earth on which all celestial bodies (stars, planets, etc.) seem to be located.
conjunction	The point in time when two celestial objects have the same celestial longitude. In the case of the Sun and a planet, superior conjunction occurs when the planet lies on the far side of the Sun (as seen from Earth). For Mercury and Venus, inferior conjuction occurs when they pass between the Sun and the Earth.
direct motion	Motion from west to east on the sky.
ecliptic	The apparent path of the Sun across the sky throughout the year. Also: the plane of the Earth's orbit in space.
elongation	The point at which an inferior planet has the greatest angular distance from the Sun, as seen from Earth.
equinox	The two points during the year when night and day have equal duration. Also: the points on the sky at which the ecliptic intersects the celestial equator. The vernal (spring) equinox is of particular importance in astronomy.
gibbous	The stage in the sequence of phases at which the illumination of a body lies between half and full. In the case of the Moon, the term is applied to phases between First Quarter and Full, and between Full and Last Quarter.
inferior planet	Either of the planets Mercury or Venus, which have orbits inside that of the Earth.
magnitude	The brightness of a star, planet or other celestial body. It is a logarithmic scale, where larger numbers indicate fainter brightness. A difference of 5 in magnitude indicates a difference of 100 in actual brightness, thus a first-magnitude star is 100 times as bright as one of sixth magnitude.
meridian	The great circle passing through the North and South Poles of a body and the observer's position; or the corresponding great circle on the celestial sphere that passes through the North and South Celestial Poles and also through the observer's zenith.
nadir	The point on the celestial sphere directly beneath the observer's feet, opposite the zenith.
occultation	The disappearance of one celestial body behind another, such as when stars or planets are hidden behind the Moon.
opposition	The point on a superior planet's orbit at which it is directly opposite the Sun in the sky.
perigee	The point on its orbit at which the Moon is closest to the Earth.
perihelion	The point on an orbit that is closest to the Sun.
retrograde motion	Motion from east to west on the sky.
superior planet	A planet that has an orbit outside that of the Earth.
vernal equinox	The point at which the Sun, in its apparent motion along the ecliptic, crosses the celestial equator from south to north. Also known as the First Point of Aries.
zenith	The point directly above the observer's head.
zodiac	A band, stretching 8° on either side of the ecliptic, within which the Moon and planets appear to move. It consists of twelve equal areas, originally named after the constellation that once lay within it.

The Constellations

There are 88 constellations covering the whole of the celestial sphere, but 4 of these in the northern hemisphere (Camelopardalis, Cassiopeia, Cepheus and Ursa Minor) can never be seen (even in part) from a latitude of 35°S, so are omitted from this table. The names themselves are expressed in Latin, and the names of stars are frequently given by Greek letters (see next page) followed by the genitive of the constellation name. The genitives and English names of the various constellations are included.

Name	Genitive	Abbr.	English name
Andromeda	Andromedae	And	Andromeda
Antlia	Antliae	Ant	Air Pump
Apus	Apodis	Aps	Bird of Paradise
Aquarius	Aquarii	Aqr	Water Bearer
Aquila	Aquilae	Aql	Eagle
Ara	Arae	Ara	Altar
Aries	Arietis	Ari	Ram
Auriga	Aurigae	Aur	Charioteer
Boötes	Boötis	Boo	Herdsman
Caelum	Caeli	Cae	Burin
Cancer	Cancri	Cnc	Crab
Canes Venatici	Canum Venaticorum	CVn	Hunting Dogs
Canis Major	Canis Majoris	CMa	Big Dog
Canis Minor	Canis Minoris	CMi	Little Dog
Capricornus	Capricorni	Cap	Sea Goat
Carina	Carinae	Car	Keel
Centaurus	Centauri	Cen	Centaur
Cetus	Ceti	Cet	Whale
Chamaeleon	Chamaeleontis	Cha	Chameleon
Circinus	Circini	Cir	Compasses
Columba	Columbae	Col	Dove
Coma Berenices	Comae Berenices	Com	Berenice's Hair
Corona Australis	Coronae Australis	CrA	Southern Crown
Corona Borealis	Coronae Borealis	CrB	Northern Crown
Corvus	Corvi	Crv	Crow
Crater	Crateris	Crt	Cup
Crux	Crucis	Cru	Southern Cross
Cygnus	Cygni	Cyg	Swan
Delphinus	Delphini	Del	Dolphin
Dorado	Doradus	Dor	Dorado
Draco	Draconis	Dra	Dragon
Equuleus	Equulei	Equ	Little Horse
Eridanus	Eridani	Eri	River Eridanus
Fornax	Fornacis	For	Furnace
Gemini	Geminorum	Gem	Twins
Grus	Gruis	Gru	Crane
Hercules	Herculis	Her	Hercules
Horologium	Horologii	Hor	Clock
Hydra	Hydrae	Hya	Water Snake
Hydrus	Hydri	Hyi	Lesser Water Snake
Indus	Indi	Ind	Indian
Lacerta	Lacertae	Lac	Lizard

Name	Genitive	Abbr.	English name
Leo	Leonis	Leo	Lion
Leo Minor	Leonis Minoris	LMi	Little Lion
Lepus	Leporis	Lep	Hare
Libra	Librae	Lib	Scales
Lupus	Lupi	Lup	Wolf
Lynx	Lyncis	Lyn	Lynx
Lyra	Lyrae	Lyr	Lyre
Mensa	Mensae	Men	Table Mountain
Microscopium	Microscopii	Mic	Microscope
Monoceros	Monocerotis	Mon	Unicorn
Musca	Muscae	Mus	Fly
Norma	Normae	Nor	Set Square
Octans	Octantis	Oct	Octant
Ophiuchus	Ophiuchi	Oph	Serpent Bearer
Orion	Orionis	Ori	Orion
Pavo	Pavonis	Pav	Peacock
Pegasus	Pegasi	Peg	Pegasus
Perseus	Persei	Per	Perseus
Phoenix	Phoenicis	Phe	Phoenix
Pictor	Pictoris	Pic	Painter's easel
Pisces	Piscium	Psc	Fishes
Piscis Austrinus	Piscis Austrini	PsA	Southern Fish
Puppis	Puppis	Pup	Stern
Pyxis	Pyxidis	Pyx	Compass
Reticulum	Reticuli	Ret	Net
Sagitta	Sagittae	Sge	Arrow
Sagittarius	Sagittarii	Sgr	Archer
Scorpius	Scorpii	Sco	Scorpion
Sculptor	Sulptoris	Scu	Sculptor
Scutum	Scuti	Sct	Shield
Serpens	Serpentis	Ser	Serpent
Sextans	Sextantis	Sex	Sextant
Taurus	Tauri	Tau	Bull
Telescopium	Telescopii	Tel	Telescope
Triangulum	Trianguli	Tri	Triangle
Triangulum Australe	Trianguli Australis	TrA	Southern Triangle
Tucana	Tucanae	Tuc	Toucan
Ursa Major	Ursae Majoris	UMa	Great Bear
Vela	Velorum	Vel	Sails
Virgo	Virginis	Vir	Virgin
Volans	Volantis	Vol	Flying Fish
Vulpecula	Vulpeculae	Vul	Fox

The Greek Alphabet

α	Alpha	ε	Epsilon	ι	Iota	ν	Nu	ρ	Rho	φ (φ)	Phi
β	Beta	ζ	Zeta	κ	Kappa	ξ	Xi	σ (ς)	Sigma	χ	Chi
γ	Gamma	η	Eta	λ	Lambda	o	Omicron	τ	Tau	ψ	Psi
δ	Delta	θ (ϑ)	Theta	μ	Mu	π	Pi	υ	Upsilon	ω	Omega

Some common asterisms

Belt of Orion	δ, ε and ζ Orionis
Cat's Eyes	λ and υ Scorpii
Circlet	γ, θ, ι, λ and κ Piscium
False Cross	ε and ι Carinae and δ and κ Velorum
Fish Hook	α, β, δ and π Scorpii
Head of Cetus	α, γ, ξ², μ and λ Ceti
Head of Hydra	δ, ε, ζ, η, ρ and σ Hydrae
Job's Coffin	α, β, γ and δ Delphini
Keystone	ε, ζ, η and π Herculis
Kids	ζ and η Aurigae
Milk Dipper	ζ, γ, σ, φ and λ Sagittarii
Pot	= Saucepan
Saucepan	ι, θ, ζ, ε, δ and η Orionis
Sickle	α, η, γ, ζ, μ and ε Leonis
Southern Pointers	α and β Centauri
Square of Pegasus	α, β and γ Pegasi with α Andromedae
Sword of Orion	θ and ι Orionis
Teapot	γ, ε, δ, λ, φ, σ, τ and ζ Sagittarii
Water Jar	γ, η, κ and ζ Aquarii
Y of Aquarius	= Water Jar

Acknowledgements

Denis Buczynski, Portmahomack, Ross-shire – p.21 (Fireball)

Dave Chapman, Dartmouth, Nova Scotia, Canada – p.77 (LMC)

European Southern Observatory – pp.53, 89, 101 (Magellanic Clouds)

Akira Fuji – p.21 (Lunar eclipse)

Bernhard Hubl – pp.43, 47, 49, 55, 59, 65, 73, 83, 85, 91, 95, 103 (Constellation photographs)

Nick James – p.28 (Comet NEOWISE)

Arthur Page, Queensland, Australia – pp.41, 71 (Constellation photographs)

Damian Peach, Hamble, UK – p.23 (Mars photo)

peresanz/Shutterstock – p.37 (Orion)

Specialist editorial support was provided by Tania de Sales Marques – Planetarium Astronomer at the Royal Observatory, part of Royal Museums Greenwich.

Further Information

Books

Bone, Neil (1993), *Observer's Handbook: Meteors*, George Philip, London & Sky Publ. Corp., Cambridge, Mass.

Cook, J., ed. (1999), *The Hatfield Photographic Lunar Atlas*, Springer-Verlag, New York

Dunlop, Storm (1999), *Wild Guide to the Night Sky*, HarperCollins, London

Dunlop, Storm (2012), *Practical Astronomy*, 3rd edn, Philip's, London

Dunlop, Storm, Rükl, Antonin & Tirion, Wil (2005), *Collins Atlas of the Night Sky*, HarperCollins, London

Ellyard, David & Tirion, Wil (2008), *Southern Sky Guide*, 3rd edn, Cambridge University Press, Cambridge

Heifetz, Milton & Tirion, Wil (2017), *A Walk through the Heavens*, 4th edn, Cambridge University Press, Cambridge

Heifetz, Milton & Tirion, Wil (2012), *A Walk through the Southern Sky*, 3rd edn, Cambridge University Press, Cambridge

O'Meara, Stephen J. (2008), *Observing the Night Sky with Binoculars*, Cambridge University Press, Cambridge

Ridpath, Ian (2018) *Star Tales*, 2nd edn, Lutterworth Press, Cambridge, UK

Ridpath, Ian, ed. (2003), *Oxford Dictionary of Astronomy*, 2nd edn, Oxford University Press, Oxford

Ridpath, Ian, ed. (2004), *Norton's Star Atlas*, 20th edn, Pi Press, New York

Ridpath, Ian & Tirion, Wil (2004), *Collins Gem – Stars*, HarperCollins, London

Ridpath, Ian & Tirion, Wil (2017), *Collins Pocket Guide Stars and Planets*, 5th edn, HarperCollins, London

Ridpath, Ian & Tirion, Wil (2019), *The Monthly Sky Guide*, 10th edn, Dover Publications, New York

Rükl, Antonín (1990), *Hamlyn Atlas of the Moon*, Hamlyn, London & Astro Media Inc., Milwaukee

Rükl, Antonín (2004), *Atlas of the Moon*, Sky Publishing Corp., Cambridge, Mass.

Scagell, Robin (2000), *Philip's Stargazing with a Telescope*, George Philip, London

Sky & Telescope (2017), *Astronomy 2018*, Australian Sky & Telescope, Quasar Publishing, Georges Hall, NSW

Stimac, Valerie (2019) *Dark Skies: A Practical Guide to Astrotourism*, Lonely Planet, Franklin, TN

Tirion, Wil (2011), *Cambridge Star Atlas*, 4th edn, Cambridge University Press, Cambridge

Tirion, Wil & Sinnott, Roger (1999), *Sky Atlas 2000.0*, 2nd edn, Sky Publishing Corp., Cambridge, Mass. & Cambridge University Press, Cambridge

Journals

Astronomy, Astro Media Corp., 21027 Crossroads Circle, P.O. Box 1612, Waukesha, WI 53187-1612 USA. http://www.astronomy.com

Astronomy Now, Pole Star Publications, PO Box 175, Tonbridge, Kent TN10 4QX UK. http://www.astronomynow.com

Sky at Night Magazine, BBC publications, London. http://skyatnightmagazine.com

Sky & Telescope, Sky Publishing Corp., Cambridge, MA 02138-1200 USA. http://www.skyandtelescope.com/

Societies

British Astronomical Association, Burlington House, Piccadilly, London W1J 0DU. http://www.britastro.org/
The principal British organization for amateur astronomers (with some professional members), particularly for those interested in carrying out observational programmes. Its membership is, however, worldwide. It publishes fully refereed, scientific papers and other material in its well-regarded journal.

Federation of Astronomical Societies, Secretary: Ken Sheldon, Whitehaven, Maytree Road, Lower Moor, Pershore, Worcs. WR10 2NY. http://www.fedastro.org.uk/fas/
An organization that is able to provide contact information for local astronomical societies in the United Kingdom.

Royal Astronomical Society, Burlington House, Piccadilly, London W1J 0BQ. http://www.ras.org.uk/
The premier astronomical society, with membership primarily drawn from professionals and experienced amateurs. It has an exceptional library and is a designated centre for the retention of certain classes of astronomical data. Its publications are the standard medium for dissemination of astronomical research.

Society for Popular Astronomy, 36 Fairway, Keyworth, Nottingham NG12 5DU.
http://www.popastro.com/
A society for astronomical beginners of all ages, which concentrates on increasing members' understanding and enjoyment, but which does have some observational programmes. Its journal is entitled *Popular Astronomy*.

Software

Planetary, Stellar and Lunar Visibility, (Planetary and eclipse freeware): Alcyone Software, Germany.
http://www.alcyone.de
Redshift, Redshift-Live. http://www.redshift-live.com/en/
Starry Night & Starry Night Pro, Sienna Software Inc., Toronto, Canada. http://www.starrynight.com

Internet sources

There are numerous sites with information about all aspects of astronomy, and all of those have numerous links. Although many amateur sites are excellent, treat any statements and data with caution. The sites listed below offer accurate information. Please note that the URLs may change. If so, use a good search engine, such as Google, to locate the information source.

Information

Astronomical data (inc. eclipses) HM Nautical Almanac Office: http://astro.ukho.gov.uk
Auroral information Michigan Tech: http://www.geo.mtu.edu/weather/aurora/
Comets JPL Solar System Dynamics: http://ssd.jpl.nasa.gov/
American Meteor Society: http://amsmeteors.org/
Deep-sky objects Saguaro Astronomy Club Database: http://www.virtualcolony.com/sac/
Eclipses: NASA Eclipse Page: http://eclipse.gsfc.nasa.gov/eclipse.html
Ice in Space (Southern Hemisphere Online Astronomy Forum) http://www.iceinspace.com.au/index.php?home
Moon (inc. Atlas) Inconstant Moon: http://www.inconstantmoon.com/
Planets Planetary Fact Sheets: http://nssdc.gsfc.nasa.gov/planetary/planetfact.html
Satellites (inc. International Space Station)
Heavens Above: http://www.heavens-above.com/
Visual Satellite Observer: http://www.satobs.org/
Star Chart http://www.skyandtelescope.com/observing/interactive-sky-watching-tools/interactive-sky-chart/
What's Visible
Skyhound: http://www.skyhound.com/sh/skyhound.html
Skyview Cafe: http://www.skyviewcafe.com

Institutes and Organizations

European Space Agency: http://www.esa.int/
International Dark-Sky Association: http://www.darksky.org/
RASC Dark Sky: https://rasc.ca/lpa/dark-sky-sites
Jet Propulsion Laboratory: http://www.jpl.nasa.gov/
Lunar and Planetary Institute: http://www.lpi.usra.edu/
National Aeronautics and Space Administration: http://www.hq.nasa.gov/
Solar Data Analysis Center: http://umbra.gsfc.nasa.gov/
Space Telescope Science Institute: http://www.stsci.edu/